Grade 6
Enrichment Math

CONTENTS

Cover Design: Beachcomber Studio

McGraw-Hill
Consumer Products

A Division of The McGraw·Hill Companies

Send all inquiries to:
McGraw-Hill Consumer Products
8787 Orion Place, 4th Floor
Columbus, Ohio 43240-4027

Printed in the United States of America.

1-57768-176-2   1 2 3 4 5 6 7 8 9 10 QPD 05 04 03 02 01 00

Name _____

WHOLE NUMBERS

WAY OUT IN SPACE

In 1772, an astronomer named Bode discovered something about
the distances of planets from the Sun. The first seven planets in
our solar system follow a number pattern.

1. Each number here is twice as big as the one before. Finish
the pattern.

      0   3   6   12   _____ _____ _____

2. Next, add 4 to each number.

    4   7   10   16

Mercury Venus Earth Mars   Jupiter Saturn Uranus

Look at the numbers that correspond to a planet. To find
the distance of the planet from the sun, multiply the planet's number
by 9,300,000 miles. Use your calculator and what you know about
place value to find the product. Start with Earth, number 10.

10 × 9,300,000 = 93,000,000 miles from the Sun

Find the distances for the other planets.

3. Mercury   _____

4. Venus   _____

5. Earth   9,300,000 × 10 = 93,000,000 miles

6. Mars   _____

7. Jupiter   _____

8. Saturn   _____

9. Uranus   _____

What happened to the number between Mars and Jupiter? There
is no planet there, but there *is* a group of *asteroids*. These rocky
objects may be a planet that exploded. Also, Neptune and Pluto,
the most distant planets, do not fit the pattern.

3

DECIMALS

CROSS THAT BRIDGE

Choose the letter of the correct standard form for each item in the left column. The letters will spell the answer to this riddle:

What is the shortest bridge in the world?

_____	1. six hundred and ten ten-thousandths	R	0.061
_____	2. sixty-one thousandths	I	0.170
_____	3. one hundred and seventy thousandths	F	0.2
_____	4. fifty-three thousand and eleven hundred-thousandths	O	0.38
_____	5. three hundred eighty thousandths	N	0.20360
_____	6. two hundredths	Y	0.7710
_____	7. one hundred and seventy-three thousandths	B	0.0610
_____	8. two tenths	E	0.771
_____	9. seven thousand, seven hundred and ten ten-thousandths	G	0.380
_____	10. thirty-eight hundredths	R	0.2036
_____	11. seven hundredths	U	0.07
_____	12. two thousand and thirty-six ten-thousandths	S	0.5301
_____	13. twenty thousand, three hundred and sixty hundred-thousandths	D	0.53011
_____	14. twenty hundredths	O	0.173
_____	15. five thousand, three hundred and one ten-thousandths	O	0.20
_____	16. seven hundred and seventy-one thousandths	E	0.02

Name _____

MAKING BAR GRAPHS

AFTER-SCHOOL SPECIALTIES

Five students asked other students in their school, "What is your favorite after-school activity?" Here are the answers they got and the number of students who gave each answer.

Aaron's results: 2—chess club, 1—baseball, 1—music lessons, 1—dance lessons, 3—TV

Bill's results: 3—swimming, 1—flute lessons, 2—TV, 2—computer club, 2—reading

Sarah's results: 1—piano lessons, 2—acting club, 2—running, 2—gymnastics

Kevin's results: 2—dance lessons, 1—acting club, 1—swimming, 1—baseball, 1—reading

Jenny's results: 3—reading, 1—chess club, 2—computer club, 1—running, 1—baseball

Make a graph to show this data.

1. Decide how you want to group the answers. Make a table showing your categories.

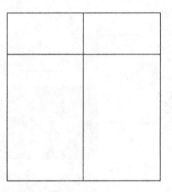

2. Decide on the labels for the two axes and make your graph.

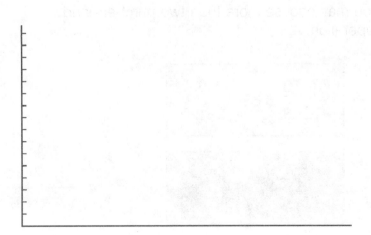

Name _____

ESTIMATING SUMS AND DIFFERENCES: ROUNDING

TARGET PRACTICE

Look at the target number in each circle. Then choose numbers
from the box whose estimated sum *or* difference will be closest to
the target. Write the addition or subtraction problem. For
problems 1–5, choose two numbers.

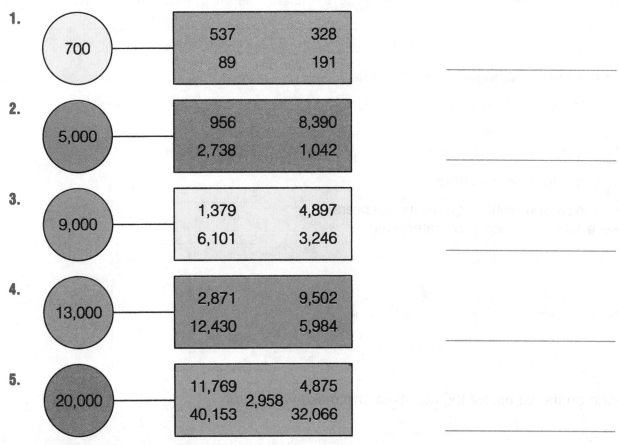

1.
700

537	328
89	191

_____

2.
5,000

956	8,390
2,738	1,042

_____

3.
9,000

1,379	4,897
6,101	3,246

_____

4.
13,000

2,871	9,502
12,430	5,984

_____

5.
20,000

11,769		4,875
	2,958	
40,153		32,066

_____

For Problems 6–7, you may choose more than two numbers and
use more than one operation.

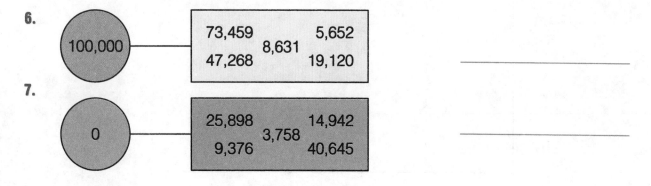

6.
100,000

73,459		5,652
	8,631	
47,268		19,120

_____

7.
0

25,898		14,942
	3,758	
9,376		40,645

_____

Name _____

FRONT-END ESTIMATIONS: SUMS AND DIFFERENCES

PATTERN PICKS

How would you complete the following?

△ is to ◭ as ◒ is to ___?___

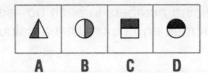

A   B   C   D

Think: △ is the same shape as ◭ , the first figure has the bottom part shaded, and the second figure has the top part shaded. Look for the same shape as ◒ , but with the top part shaded. The correct answer is D.

Now try this one.

⁛ is to ⁞ as ⸭ is to ___?___

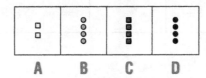

A   B   C   D

Which answer is correct? Explain your reasoning. _____

_____

Write the letter of the correct answer.

	A	B	C	D
1. △ is to ▼ as ⏢ is to _____.	▽	▶	▼	◁
2. ⠃ is to ⠆ as ⠣ is to _____.	⠿	⠶	⠪	⠿
3. └ is to ⌟ as E is to _____.	⌐	⌐	⊔	⊐
4. ▲▲ is to ▲▲ as ●● is to _____.	▲▲	▲▲	●●	●●
5. ××× is to ×× as ●●● is to _____.	●●●	●●●●	×××	○○○
6. ■ is to ▟ as ● is to _____.	●	◖	◗	◠
7. ⠒ is to ⠇ as ⠿ is to _____.	▫	⠇	⠒	▪

ADDING AND SUBTRACTING WHOLE NUMBERS

SQUARE DEAL

Fill in the missing numbers in each box so the addition problems are correct across and down. Use a calculator if you wish.

25,145	+		=	57,313
+		+		+
13,481	+	7,519	=	
=		=		=
38,626	+		=	78,313

	+	25,361	=	40,039
+		+		+
	+	10,762	=	
=		=		=
47,569	+		=	83,692

	+	26,108	=	38,306
+		+		+
	+		=	
=		=		=
23,657	+		=	81,592

Name

SOLVING EQUATIONS

EXTREME MEASURES

How do you measure poison ivy?

Solve each equation. Then draw a line to connect each pair of equations that have the same answer. (Use a ruler and draw a line between the dots.) The letters that are not crossed out will answer the riddle.

$n + 7 = 14$ $n =$ ___ •

o   b   d
                           • $6 - n = 4$ $n =$ ___

$n - 3 = 6$ $n =$ ___ •   y

                              • $n + 2 = 14$ $n =$ ___

$6 + n = 12$ $n =$ ___ •   • $n - 2 = 17$ $n =$ ___

a

$3 + n = 8$ $n =$ ___ •   y • $n + 3 = 10$ $n =$ ___

$n - 14 = 2$ $n =$ ___ • i   • $n - 2 = 8$ $n =$ ___

$n - 5 = 5$ $n =$ ___ •   • $n + 3 = 9$ $n =$ ___

$n + 6 = 19$ $n =$ ___ • t   • $n - 1 = 10$ $n =$ ___
                                 s

$n - 7 = 4$ $n =$ ___ • r   • $n + 5 = 10$ $n =$ ___

                        c

$n + 8 = 16$ $n =$ ___ •   f   • $n + 6 = 15$ $n =$ ___

n

$20 - n = 5$ $n =$ ___ •   • $n - 4 = 12$ $n =$ ___

$n + 1 = 3$ $n =$ ___ • r   • $n + 9 = 17$ $n =$ ___

$n - 8 = 4$ $n =$ ___ • h   • $16 - n = 3$ $n =$ ___

                         e
$20 - n = 16$ $n =$ ___ •   • $n + 1 = 16$ $n =$ ___

$n + 5 = 19$ $n =$ ___ •   s   • $5 - n = 1$ $n =$ ___

$n + 1 = 20$ $n =$ ___ • s   • $n - 3 = 11$ $n =$ ___

$n - 7 = 14$ $n =$ ___ • e   • $n - 1 = 20$ $n =$ ___

$n + 3 = 21$ $n =$ ___ •   t   • $n - 4 = 14$ $n =$ ___

9

MAKING LINE GRAPHS

COMMON QUALITIES

Here are two sets of numbers. Set A has odd numbers. Set B has even numbers:

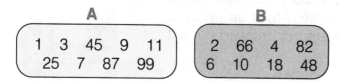

A
1   3   45   9   11
25   7   87   99

B
2   66   4   82
6   10   18   48

Here the two sets overlap. The numbers that fit in set C where the sets overlap have something else in common. They are under 20. One set is even and under 20; one set is odd and under 20.

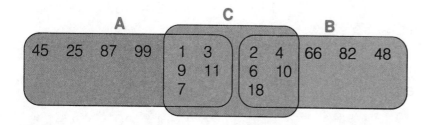

A   **C**   **B**
45   25   87   99   1   3   2   4   66   82   48
                     9   11   6   10
                     7   18

Look at each of these diagrams. Write what the numbers in sets A and B have in common.

1.
A
0.3   1.7   3.2
0.5   0.08   41.62
9.1

B
1   12   25
108   15
17   16

2.
A
15   91
27   1   4
16   46

B
101   197
104   125   118
106

For this example, write what the numbers that fit in set C have in common, too.

3.
A   **C**   **B**
15   25   105   156   126   6   36
35   5   115   106   76   26
65   175   186   16

MENTAL MATH: MULTIPLYING

WHO'S WHO?

Anne, Beth, Charles, and David go to four different schools. The
schools are Lincoln, Washington, Cleveland, and Roosevelt. Write
the school that each student goes to. Use the clues below to help you.

Anne _____

Beth _____

Charles _____

David _____

CLUES

1. The person who goes to Washington is a boy.

2. Charles used to go to Washington, but he changed schools
   this year.

3. Anne's school played softball against Roosevelt last month.

4. The student at Roosevelt is a girl.

5. Charles's cousin lives on the other side of town and goes to
   Lincoln.

You might find it helpful to fill in this chart as you get information
about the students. Write X for no and √ for yes.

	Lincoln	Washington	Cleveland	Roosevelt
Anne				
Beth				
Charles				
David				

Name _____

Multiplying

SCRAMBLED NUMBERS

Use the numbers in the box to write the factors and the product
for each multiplication problem.

1.
| 2 |
| 1 |
| 3 |

```
        9 _ _
  ×         3
  2 , 7 6 _
```

2.
| 8 |
| 1 |
| 3 |

```
      4 _ 7
  ×       _
  3 , 9 _ 6
```

3.
| 7 |
| 3 |
| 0 |

```
      4 _ 8
  ×       9
  _ , 6 _ 2
```

4.
| 0 | 1 |
| 0 | 0 |

```
  1 , _ 2 _
  ×       8
  8 , _ 6 _
```

5.
| 6 | 2 |
| 5 | 5 |

```
  2 , _ 7 1
  ×       _
  1 _ , 4 _ 6
```

6.
0	4
0	5
2	

```
    _ , _ _ 5
  ×         7
  _ 8 , 0 3 _
```

7.
2	0
1	8
5	

```
      9 _ _
  ×       _
  1 , _ 3 _
```

8.
1	6
3	3
2	8

```
      7 _ _
  ×       _
  2 , _ _ _
```

MULTIPLYING GREATER NUMBERS

SERIOUS SERIES

These numbers follow a pattern. Each number is 12 times the number before it.

      3   36   432   5,184

The next two numbers in the series are 62,208 (5,184 × 12) and 746,496 (62,208 × 12).

For each series, describe the pattern. Then fill in the next two numbers in each series. Use a calculator to help you. (*Hint:* Remember, not every series uses multiplication.)

1. 4 64 1,024 _____ _____   _____

2. 5 10 15 20 25 _____ _____   _____

3. 3 51 867 _____ _____   _____

4. 23 184 1,472 11,776 _____ _____   _____

5. 3 8 40 45 225 230 _____ _____   _____

6. 6 13 91 98 686 693 _____ _____   _____

7. 12 10 660 658 43,428 _____ _____   _____

8. 19 10 90 81 729 _____ _____   _____

9. 124 248 496 992 _____ _____   _____

10. 375 75 600 300 2,400 _____ _____   _____

11. Write a series using a multiplication pattern. Give it to a friend to solve.

_____

12. Write a series with a pattern that uses addition *or* subtraction and multiplication. Give it to a friend to solve.

_____

EXPONENTS

EXPONENTIALLY SPEAKING

Remember that you can use exponents to show multiplication
when all the factors are the same.

$$5 \times 5 \times 5 \times 5 = 5^4$$

Now study the multiplication shown below.

$(3 \times 3 \times 3)$	$\times$	(3×3)	$=$	$3 \times 3 \times 3 \times 3 \times 3$
27	$\times$	9	$=$	243

Write the exponents and the product in each problem. Then
check that the products are correct. Use a calculator.

1.
$$3 \times 3 \times 3 \quad = \quad 3^{\square} \quad =$$
$$\underline{\times \qquad 3 \times 3} \quad = \quad \underline{\times\ 3^{\square}} \quad =$$
$$3 \times 3 \times 3 \times 3 \quad = \quad 3^{\square} \quad =$$

$$\begin{array}{r} 2\ 7 \\ \times\ \square \\ \hline \square\square\square \end{array}$$

2.
$$4 \times 4 \times 4 \times 4 \quad = \quad 4^{\square} \quad =$$
$$\underline{\times \qquad\qquad 4 \times 4} \quad = \quad \underline{\times\ 4^{\square}} \quad =$$
$$4 \times 4 \times 4 \times 4 \times 4 \times 4 \quad = \quad 4^{\square} \quad =$$

$$\begin{array}{r} \square\square \\ \times\ \square\square\square \\ \hline \square,\square\square\square \end{array}$$

3.
$$2 \times 2 \times 2 \quad = \quad 2^{\square} \quad =$$
$$\underline{\times \qquad 2 \times 2 \times 2} \quad = \quad \underline{\times\ 2^{\square}} \quad =$$
$$2 \times 2 \times 2 \times 2 \times 2 \times 2 \quad = \quad 2^{\square} \quad =$$

$$\begin{array}{r} \square \\ \times\ \square \\ \hline \square\square \end{array}$$

4. Can you write a rule that tells how to multiply two or more
   numbers in exponent form? What must be true about the base
   of each exponential number?

_____

_____

Use your rule to write the answer to these problems. Then write
the factors and products in standard form. Check that the
products are correct. Use a calculator.

5. $4^2 \times 4^2 =$ _____   _____

6. $7^4 \times 7^3 =$ _____   _____

7. $12^3 \times 12^2 =$ _____   _____

8. $2^2 \times 2^3 \times 2^4 =$ _____   _____

MENTAL MATH: MULTIPLYING DECIMALS

MULTIPLICATION MAKES MAGIC

1. Multiply. Write each product in the box below that has the same letter as the problem. Leave **o** and **p** blank for now.

   a. 0.072×10 _____

   b. 0.00036×100 _____

   c. 0.012×100 _____

   d. $0.0018 \times 1{,}000$ _____

   e. 0.108×10 _____

   f. 0.0192×100 _____

   g. $0.0006 \times 1{,}000$ _____

   h. 0.048×10 _____

   i. 0.0084×100 _____

   j. 0.024×10 _____

   k. $0.000132 \times 10{,}000$ _____

   l. $0.00168 \times 1{,}000$ _____

   m. 0.0144×100 _____

   n. $0.000156 \times 10{,}000$ _____

   o. _____

   p. _____

2. In a magic square, the sum of each row, column, and diagonal should be the same. Fill in the two missing boxes so that you have a magic square. Then write multiplication problems for letters **o** and **p** above.

a.	b.	c.	d.
e.	f.	g.	h.
i.	j.	k.	l.
m.	n.	o.	p.

The magic sum is

_____ .

Name _____

MULTIPLYING DECIMALS

PUZZLING NUMBERS

Multiply. Then find each answer in the grid below. Write the word that matches each number in the grid.

1. is

$$4.5 \times 0.09$$

2. funny

$$11.36 \times 9.98$$

3. both

$$0.89 \times 4.39$$

4. have

$$55.1 \times 0.15$$

5. A

$$3.44 \times 0.08$$

6. story

$$0.578 \times 7.7$$

7. pencil

$$0.996 \times 5.6$$

8. They

$$0.566 \times 0.45$$

9. a

$$4.781 \times 3.5$$

10. like

$$11.41 \times 0.55$$

11. a

$$0.981 \times 0.33$$

12. point

$$0.877 \times 0.29$$

0.2752	5.5776	0.405	6.2755
_____	_____	_____	_____
16.7335	113.3728	4.4506	0.2547
_____	_____	_____	_____
3.9071	8.265	0.32373	0.25433
_____	_____	_____	_____

Name _____

RELATING MULTIPLICATION AND DIVISION

THE BLACK BOX

The black box contains a rule that changes numbers. Look at the numbers on the left. Then see what they become when they come out of the black box.

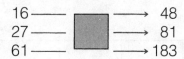

```
16 ──────┐    ┌────→ 48
27 ──────┤    ├────→ 81
61 ──────┘    └────→ 183
```

The rule inside the black box must be to multiply the number that goes in by 3.

Look at each of these examples. Write the rule. Then write the output for the last number. The rules may have more than one step, such as multiply by 3 and add 1.

1.
```
 7                      105
 1  ──→  [   ]  ──→      15
12                      180
14                      ___
```
Rule: _____

2.
```
 2                       5
 6  ──→  [   ]  ──→      13
10                      21
29                      ___
```
Rule: _____

3.
```
15                      38
 3  ──→  [   ]  ──→     14
10                      28
17.5                    ___
```
Rule: _____

4.
```
  1                     11
  2  ──→  [   ]  ──→    16
 10                     56
193                     ___
```
Rule: _____

5.
```
 20                      6
100  ──→  [   ]  ──→    26
 28                      8
1.2                     ___
```
Rule: _____

Name

MENTAL MATH: DIVISION PATTERNS

CODE BREAKER

The letters A to J stand for the numbers 0 to 9. Two letters stand
for a two-digit number. Look at the problems below. They will help
you break the code. Write the number that each letter stands for.

A	B	C	D	E	F	G	H	I	J

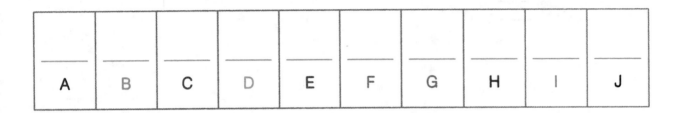

$$\begin{array}{r} B \\ \times A \\ \hline B \end{array} \qquad \begin{array}{r} J \\ \times I \\ \hline I \end{array} \qquad \begin{array}{r} I \\ + D \\ \hline D \end{array} \qquad \begin{array}{r} F \\ + F \\ \hline AI \end{array}$$

$$\begin{array}{r} F \\ - A \\ \hline E \end{array} \qquad \begin{array}{r} F \\ \times C \\ \hline AI \end{array} \qquad \begin{array}{r} C \\ + E \\ \hline J \end{array} \qquad C \overline{)AJ}^{\,D}$$

$$J + A = B \qquad E \times H = AC \qquad F + C + C = G$$

18

DIVIDING BY ONE-DIGIT NUMBERS

PUZZLING PATTERN

Write the missing numbers and signs. Use a calculator to help you. (There is more than one right answer in some places.)

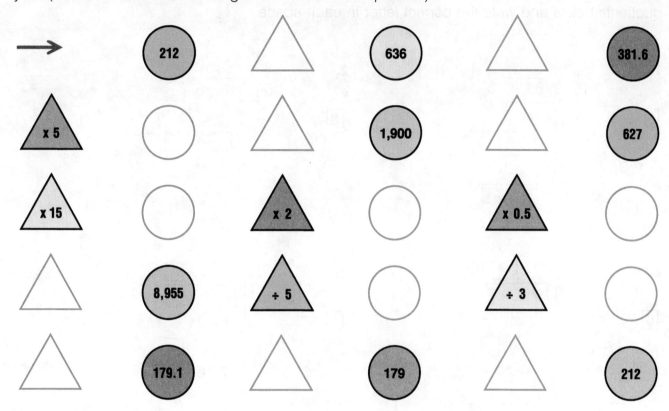

Create your own pattern puzzle in the space below.

DIVIDING BY TWO-DIGIT NUMBERS

MISSING DIGITS

Which state is nicknamed the *Show Me State*? To find out, write the missing digits in each division problem. Then find the quotients below and write the correct letter in each space.

1.

S

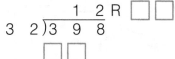
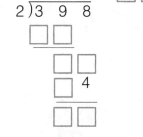

2.

O

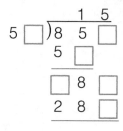

3.

U

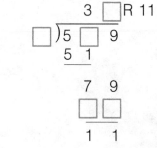

```
        2 □R 7
   □□)9 0 7
      9 0
         □
         □
         7
```

4.

I

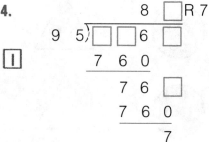

5.

M

```
        3 □R 11
   □)5 □ 9
     5 1
      7 9
     □□
      1 1
```

6.

R

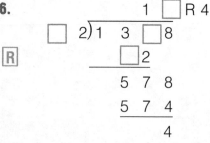

The <u>Show Me State</u> is ___ ___ ___ ___ ___ ___ ___ ___

34R11 88R7 12R14 12R14   15   20R7   17R4   80R7

Name

DIVIDING: CHANGING ESTIMATES

PUZZLING NUMBERS

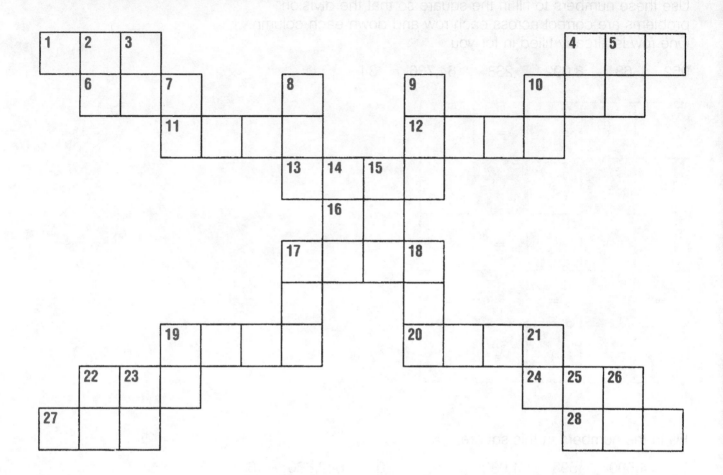

Across

1. 10,900 ÷ 25
4. ___ ÷ 7 = 79
6. ___ ÷ 4 = 157
10. ___ ÷ 2 = 52
11. ___ ÷ 60 = 26
12. ___ ÷ 47 = 58
13. ___ ÷ 88 = 52
16. ___ ÷ 7 = 8

17. ___ ÷ 4 = 711
19. ___ ÷ 25 = 200
20. ___ ÷ 82 = 28
22. 696 ÷ 6
24. ___ ÷ 4 = 131
27. ___ ÷ 7 = 94
28. ___ ÷ 10 = 23

Down

2. 540 ÷ 15
3. 5,084 ÷ 82
4. 450 ÷ 9
5. 5,292 ÷ ___ = 98
7. 2,025 ÷ 25
8. ___ ÷ 151 = 4
9. 630 ÷ 5
10. 256 ÷ 16
14. ___ ÷ 62 = 9

15. ___ ÷ 191 = 4
17. 1,600 ÷ 8
18. 1,206 ÷ 3
19. 448 ÷ 8
21. 520 ÷ 8
22. 1,380 ÷ 92
23. 36 ÷ 2
25. 990 ÷ 45
26. 2,365 ÷ 55

DIVIDING GREATER NUMBERS

SQUARE OFF

Use these numbers to fill in the square so that the division problems are correct across each row and down each column. One row is already filled in for you.

952   68   8,092   238   64,736   34

	÷		=	
÷		÷		÷
	÷		=	
=		=		=
8	÷	4	=	2

Fill in the numbers in this square.

7   4,590   595   1,080   140   20   642,600   85   54

	÷		=	
÷		÷		÷
	÷		=	
=		=		=
	÷		=	

MULTIPLICATION AND DIVISION EQUATIONS

DEEP DEPTHS

Mt. Everest is the highest point on the earth. What is the lowest point? To find out, solve each equation. Write the letter above each question in the space below that matches n. (Write the letter everywhere there is a matching number.)

B
$6n = 36$

E
$n \div 4 = 4$

D
$7n = 49$

I
$100 \div n = 10$

Y
$n \div 4 = 3$

L
$n \div 20 = 6$

R
$7n = 14$

D
$5n = 55$

N
$n \div 12 = 12$

T
$n \div 16 = 5$

M
$10n = 130$

R
$15n = 45$

A
$2n = 28$

C
$n \div 7 = 21$

A
$96 \div n = 12$

T
$4n = 60$

13	14	2	10	16

6	12	2	7

120	14	144	11

14	144	80	14	3	147	15	10	147	14

MENTAL MATH: DIVIDING PATTERNS WITH POWERS OF 10

A SHRINKING VIOLET?

What gets shorter as it grows older?

Divide mentally. Then arrange the answers from least to greatest
on the lines below. Write the letter for each problem above it.
You'll have the answer to the riddle.

L
78.2 ÷ 100 _____

R
3.2 ÷ 1,000 _____

E
14.33 ÷ 10 _____

D
67.44 ÷ 100 _____

N
0.078 ÷ 10 _____

B
0.113 ÷ 100 _____

N
122.3 ÷ 1,000 _____

I
34.6 ÷ 1,000 _____

N
566.1 ÷ 1,000 _____

C
1.8 ÷ 10 _____

U
2.03 ÷ 1,000 _____

G
14.92 ÷ 100 _____

A
45.1 ÷ 100 _____

A
0.3 ÷ 1,000 _____

_____ _____ _____ _____ _____ _____ _____

_____ _____ _____ _____ _____ _____ _____

Name

ZEROS IN THE QUOTIENT AND THE DIVIDEND

ZEROED OUT

Fill in the missing numbers in these division problems.

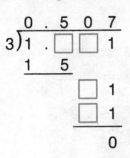

1.
```
      0 . 5 0 7
  3)1 . □ □ 1
    1 5
       □ 1
       □ 1
          0
```

2.
```
          1 . 9
 1 1)□ □ . 9
     1 1
         9 □
         9 □
           0
```

3.
```
      0 . 1 1 □
  7)0 . 8 □ □
        □
      1 □
        7
        3 □
        3 5
           0
```

4.
```
        2 . □ 6
 □ □)2 4 . 7 2
     2 4
        7 □
        7 □
           0
```

5.
```
      0 . □ □ 3
 2 1)2 . 1 □ 3
     2 1
        □ 3
        6 □
           0
```

6.
```
      1 . 1 □
  8)□ . 0 4
    8
    □ 0
      8
      2 4
      2 4
         0
```

7.
```
      □ . □ 1
  9)8 □ . □ 9
    8 1
          9
          □
          0
```

8.
```
      0 . 1 □ 4
 3 3)3 . □ 3 2
     3 3
        □ 3 2
        1 □
            0
```

9.
```
      1 . 5 □ 6
  4)□ . 3 □ 4
    4
    □ 3
    □ 0
      3 □
      □ 8
        2 4
        2 4
           0
```

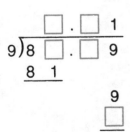

DIVIDING DECIMALS BY DECIMALS

IF THE NUMBER FITS

For each problem, pick a divisor and quotient from the baskets to make a correct division problem. Use each number exactly once.

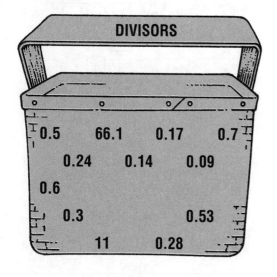

DIVISORS

0.5   66.1   0.17   0.7
0.24   0.14   0.09
0.6
0.3   0.53
11   0.28

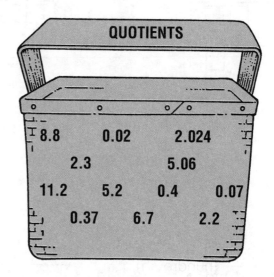

QUOTIENTS

8.8   0.02   2.024
2.3   5.06
11.2   5.2   0.4   0.07
0.37   6.7   2.2

1. 0.6072 ÷ _____ = _____

2. 1.608 ÷ _____ = _____

3. 5.6 ÷ _____ = _____

4. 1.232 ÷ _____ = _____

5. 3.542 ÷ _____ = _____

6. 1.166 ÷ _____ = _____

7. 0.391 ÷ _____ = _____

8. 0.468 ÷ _____ = _____

9. 0.427 ÷ _____ = _____

10. 0.1036 ÷ _____ = _____

11. 0.012 ÷ _____ = _____

12. 4.4 ÷ _____ = _____

Name _____

ROUNDING DECIMAL QUOTIENTS

UNCOVER THE FACTS

What baseball player's record for the most home runs lasted from 1935 to 1974?

To find the facts, use your ruler to connect the problems on the left with the answers on the right. Round to the nearest place indicated in parentheses. Use your calculator.

2.5 ÷ 8	(tenth)	B	0.398
3.31 ÷ 7	(tenth)	Y A R	0.03
0.0976 ÷ 8	(hundredth)	O C	0.144
6.77 ÷ 17	(thousandth)	B	0.847
0.25 ÷ 8	(hundredth)	G E E	0.5
17.8 ÷ 5	(tenth)	B R	0.3
2.55 ÷ 5	(hundredth)	R U	0.4
89.3 ÷ 6	(thousandth)	L A S M T	0.01
7.62 ÷ 9	(thousandth)	B V	14.883
7.145 ÷ 18	(tenth)	N H E	3.6
4.887 ÷ 34	(thousandth)		0.51

Rearrange the letters that are not crossed out in the spaces below.

_____ _____ _____ _____ _____ _____ _____ _____

Now solve this problem to find out how many home runs the player hit. Round each division step to the nearest hundredth. Then round the answer to a whole number.

(8.273 ÷ 1.2) × (459.72 ÷ 9) × (16.98 ÷ 8.37) = _____

Name

ORDER OF OPERATIONS

FIGURE IT OUT

In the pattern below, there are two sets of figures. In each set, the figures are related in the same way: The second figure is a smaller version of the first.

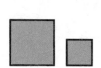 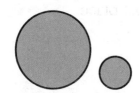

In each of the following patterns, ring the letter of the figure that completes the second set. The figures should be related in the same way in each set.

1. | **A** **B** **C**

2. | **A** **B** **C**

3. | **A** **B** **C**

4. | **A** **B** **C**

5. | **A** **B** **C**

6. | **A** **B** **C**

7. | **A** **B** **C**

28

MEAN, MEDIAN, MODE, AND RANGE

MAKE THE GRADE

Imagine that you are teacher for a day. Here are your students' scores on a math test. There are a possible 100 points on the test. What grade will you give each student?

In order to be fair, you should use some statistics to help you. You can calculate the mean, mode, median, and range of the scores. Make up a scale telling what scores get a passing grade (A, B, C, or D) and what scores fail (F).

Student	Score	Grade
1	81	
2	95	
3	86	
4	76	
5	81	
6	94	
7	73	
8	81	
9	100	
10	52	
11	79	
12	37	
13	86	
14	75	
15	93	
16	73	
17	76	
18	90	
19	87	
20	80	

Which type of statistic was most helpful in grading the test? _____

How many of each grade did you give?

A _____   B _____   C _____   D _____   F _____

What grade did you give to a test score that was the mean on the test? _____

What grade did you give to a test score that was the median on the test? _____

What grade did you give to a test score that was the mode on the test? _____

FACTORS AND GREATEST COMMON FACTOR

DAFFY DINO DEFINITION

Which dinosaur was the fastest?

Using a ruler, draw a line from the numbers on the left to their greatest common factor (GCF) on the right. The letters that remain will answer the question. Write the letters in order, reading from top to bottom, in the blank below.

1.   12, 28 •   B   P   • 15

2.   40, 4, 2 •   R   • 4

3. 75, 25, 15 •   R   • 12

4.   12, 24 •   N   O   O   • 20

5.   30, 40 •   N   T   • 16

6. 45, 60, 75 •   T   O   • 2

7.   60, 80 •   S   O   • 5

8. 16, 48, 80 • S   • 10

9.   12, 18 •   A   U   • 8

10.   14, 21 •   R   R   • 6

11. 45, 72, 90 •   U   S   • 9

12.   64, 24 •   U   S   • 7

The fastest dinosaur was the _____

Name

MULTIPLES AND LEAST COMMON MULTIPLE

CAREFUL ARRANGEMENTS

How can you arrange four 3s so the value is 36? Here is one way:

$$(3 + 3) \times (3 + 3) \rightarrow 6 \times 6 = 36$$

In the puzzles below, you can use any operation signs you choose, as well as decimal points or fractions.

1. Arrange four 5s so the value is 100.

_____

2. Arrange four 9s so the value is 153.

_____

3. Arrange four 9s so the value is 20.

_____

4. Arrange four 5s so the value is 2.5.

_____

5. Arrange four 3s so the value is 34.

_____

6. Arrange five 3s so the value is 17.

_____

7. Arrange five 2s so the value is 0.

_____

FRACTIONS AND EQUIVALENT FRACTIONS

FRACTURED FAIRY TALE

What fairy tale is about some talking vegetables?

Write an equivalent fraction for each of the following fractions.
Then find the answers under the lines below. Write the letter for
each fraction on the line. The first letter has been filled in.

H $\frac{3}{8} = \frac{}{16}$ **A** $\frac{4}{5} = \frac{}{10}$ **A** $\frac{7}{8} = \frac{}{16}$ **K** $\frac{6}{10} = \frac{}{5}$ **L** $\frac{9}{10} = \frac{}{20}$ **T** $\frac{1}{4} = \frac{}{16}$

A $\frac{5}{10} = \frac{}{20}$ **E** $\frac{3}{5} = \frac{}{10}$ **A** $\frac{2}{4} = \frac{}{8}$ **K** $\frac{8}{10} = \frac{}{5}$ **N** $\frac{6}{8} = \frac{}{4}$ **D** $\frac{10}{16} = \frac{}{8}$

B $\frac{4}{10} = \frac{}{5}$ **C** $\frac{6}{12} = \frac{}{4}$ **S** $\frac{14}{20} = \frac{}{10}$ **T** $\frac{3}{9} = \frac{}{3}$ **N** $\frac{3}{6} = \frac{}{12}$ **E** $\frac{1}{3} = \frac{}{6}$

J ___ ___ ___
   $\frac{8}{10}$ $\frac{2}{4}$ $\frac{3}{5}$

___ ___ ___
$\frac{14}{16}$ $\frac{3}{4}$ $\frac{5}{8}$

___ ___ ___
$\frac{4}{16}$ $\frac{6}{16}$ $\frac{6}{10}$

___ ___ ___ ___ ___
$\frac{2}{5}$ $\frac{2}{6}$ $\frac{4}{8}$ $\frac{6}{12}$ $\frac{7}{10}$

___ ___ ___ ___
$\frac{1}{3}$ $\frac{10}{20}$ $\frac{18}{20}$ $\frac{4}{5}$

MIXED NUMBERS

CURIOUS CODE

In each problem, the numbers have been replaced by letters. Each letter always stands for the same number. It may be a 1-digit number or a 2-digit number. All answers are fractions or mixed numbers written in simplest terms.

Use the clue and logic to decide what number each letter stands for. Write the 12 letters and numbers on the lines below.

CLUE: L = 2

$$\frac{L}{F} = \frac{S}{L}$$

$$\frac{A}{F} = S\frac{S}{F}$$

$$\frac{E}{A} = S\frac{F}{A}$$

$$\frac{I}{E} = \frac{S}{I}$$

$$\frac{O}{F} = L\frac{I}{F}$$

$$\frac{H}{L} = I\frac{S}{L}$$

$$\frac{C}{F} = I$$

$$\frac{T}{C} = \frac{S}{L}$$

$$\frac{B}{T} = S\frac{S}{I}$$

$$\frac{Y}{F} = L\frac{S}{L}$$

Letter	Number	Letter	Number
L	2		

Now replace each number with its corresponding letter to get the answer to this riddle:

"How is a frog like a baseball player?"

___ ___ ___ ___ ___ ___ ___ ___ ___ ___

___ ___ ___ ___

COMPARING AND ORDERING

DAFFYNITIONS

To answer each riddle, write each group of fractions and mixed numbers in order from least to greatest. Write the letter of each number below the line.

What do you call the place where school lunches are made?

O	U	R	S	O	H	M	M
1	$\frac{2}{9}$	$\frac{2}{3}$	$\frac{1}{3}$	$\frac{7}{9}$	$\frac{4}{9}$	$\frac{1}{6}$	$1\frac{1}{3}$

___ ___ ___ ___ ___ ___ ___ ___

What do you call a twisted doughnut?

T	P	L	E	Z	E	R
$\frac{7}{12}$	$\frac{2}{12}$	$1\frac{1}{12}$	$\frac{1}{2}$	$\frac{3}{4}$	$\frac{11}{12}$	$\frac{1}{4}$

___ ___ ___ ___ ___ ___ ___

What do you call a cucumber in a sour mood?

I	L	K	P	C	E
$\frac{3}{16}$	$\frac{7}{16}$	$\frac{3}{8}$	$\frac{1}{8}$	$\frac{10}{32}$	$\frac{4}{8}$

___ ___ ___ ___ ___ ___

What do you call a song played on an automobile radio?

R	C	A	O	O	N	T
$1\frac{3}{8}$	$\frac{5}{8}$	$\frac{3}{4}$	$1\frac{3}{4}$	$1\frac{5}{8}$	$1\frac{11}{12}$	$1\frac{5}{12}$

___ ___ ___ ___ ___ ___ ___

Name _____

ROUNDING FRACTIONS AND MIXED NUMBERS

FRACTION ACTION

You can use mental math to decide if a fraction is greater than $\frac{1}{2}$.

Example: Is $\frac{3}{5} > \frac{1}{2}$?

Double the numerator.	$2 \times 3 = 6$
If the result is greater than the denominator,	$6 > 5$
the fraction is greater than $\frac{1}{2}$.	so $\frac{3}{5} > \frac{1}{2}$

Is the fraction greater than $\frac{1}{2}$? Write YES or NO.

1. $\frac{5}{9}$ _____ 2. $\frac{3}{7}$ _____ 3. $\frac{4}{11}$ _____ 4. $\frac{7}{15}$ _____

5. $\frac{7}{10}$ _____ 6. $\frac{8}{19}$ _____ 7. $\frac{13}{21}$ _____ 8. $\frac{11}{17}$ _____

In the maze below, find a path from START to END. Use only fractions that are greater than $\frac{1}{2}$. You may go up, down, across, or diagonally, but do not cross a number more than once.

$\frac{15}{16}$	$\frac{7}{15}$	$\frac{12}{30}$	$\frac{10}{24}$	$\frac{45}{90}$	END
$\frac{26}{50}$	$\frac{34}{70}$	$\frac{18}{32}$	$\frac{4}{7}$	$\frac{12}{25}$	$\frac{7}{11}$
$\frac{13}{20}$	$\frac{8}{15}$	$\frac{9}{20}$	$\frac{345}{700}$	$\frac{146}{300}$	$\frac{80}{150}$
$\frac{8}{14}$	$\frac{5}{12}$	$\frac{5}{13}$	$\frac{66}{130}$	$\frac{41}{81}$	$\frac{3}{7}$
$\frac{16}{33}$	$\frac{17}{33}$	$\frac{5}{10}$	$\frac{44}{87}$	$\frac{42}{90}$	$\frac{22}{44}$
START	$\frac{14}{28}$	$\frac{5}{9}$	$\frac{65}{130}$	$\frac{3}{5}$	$\frac{8}{18}$

35

CUSTOMARY UNITS OF LENGTH

GOING TO GREAT LENGTH

Arrange these items from longest to shortest. (You'll have to find a way to compare their lengths first, since they are all given in different units.)

Remember, a mile is 5,280 feet.

White Sea—Baltic Canal, Soviet Union	141 mi
Golden Gate Bridge, California	1,400 yd
Simplon I Tunnel, Switzerland to Italy	12.3 mi
Sydney Harbor Bridge, Australia	19,800 in.
Panama Canal, Panama	50.7 mi
Mackinac Straits Bridge, Michigan	45,600 in.
Verrazano Narrows Bridge, New York	4,260 ft
Welland Canal, Canada	49,280 yd
Suez Canal, Egypt	100.6 mi
New River Gorge Bridge, West Virginia	1,700 ft
Rokko Tunnel, Japan	633,600 in.
Northern Line Subway Tunnel, England	30,488 yd

1. _____

2. _____

3. _____

4. _____

5. _____

6. _____

7. _____

8. _____

9. _____

10. _____

11. _____

12. _____

FRACTIONS, MIXED NUMBERS, AND DECIMALS

CROSSHATCH

Try to find a decimal in columns 3 and 4 that matches each fraction or mixed number in columns 1 and 2. When you find a match, cross out both the numbers and the letters next to them. A match may be found in any row. An example is done for you.

COLUMN 1	COLUMN 2	COLUMN 3	COLUMN 4
~~C $1\frac{1}{10}$~~	A $\frac{5}{10}$	U 0.34	A 0.5
E $\frac{75}{1,000}$	P $4\frac{89}{100}$	E 6.25	T 0.11
O $\frac{1}{4}$	E $\frac{3}{4}$	B 0.25	~~D 1.1~~
T $\frac{3}{8}$	I $7\frac{99}{100}$	E 0.75	A 4.089
B $2\frac{5}{1,000}$	R $6\frac{1}{8}$	Q 9.855	E 2.005
T $\frac{6}{10}$	I $1\frac{1}{4}$	N 6.125	E 9.12
N $\frac{12}{10}$	N $9\frac{1}{2}$	A 7.099	S 7.5
E $\frac{4}{10}$	O $\frac{32}{1,000}$	M 0.4	T 1.25
H $3\frac{2}{100}$	T $\frac{7}{10}$	L 1.02	L 2.8

Now write the letters that are left in each column on the line.
Unscramble each group of letters to spell a familiar mathematical word.

COLUMN 1 _____   _____

COLUMN 2 _____   _____

COLUMN 3 _____   _____

COLUMN 4 _____   _____

ADDING FRACTIONS: UNLIKE DENOMINATORS

THE MISSING LINK

Fill in the boxes with the missing numbers. Each fraction in these
problems should be in its simplest form.

1.
$$\frac{1}{2}$$
$$+ \frac{\square}{\square}$$
$$\overline{\quad \frac{3}{4} \quad}$$

2.
$$\frac{\square}{6}$$
$$+ \frac{\square}{3}$$
$$\overline{\quad \frac{1}{2} \quad}$$

3.
$$\frac{3}{8}$$
$$\frac{1}{\square}$$
$$\overline{\quad \frac{5}{8} \quad}$$

4.
$$\frac{5}{\square}$$
$$+ \frac{3}{\square}$$
$$\overline{\quad \frac{1}{2} \quad}$$

5.
$$\frac{1}{3}$$
$$+ \frac{\square}{4}$$
$$\overline{\quad \frac{7}{12} \quad}$$

6.
$$\frac{1}{3}$$
$$+ \frac{\square}{6}$$
$$\overline{\quad 1\frac{1}{\square} \quad}$$

7.
$$\frac{\square}{10}$$
$$+ \frac{9}{10}$$
$$\overline{\quad 1\frac{1}{\square} \quad}$$

8.
$$\frac{\square}{4}$$
$$+ \frac{\square}{8}$$
$$\overline{\quad \square\frac{3}{\square} \quad}$$

Name _____

SUBTRACTING FRACTIONS: UNLIKE DENOMINATORS

PICK A PAIR

1. Which two numbers have a sum of exactly $\frac{1}{2}$?

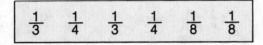

$$\frac{1}{3} \quad \frac{1}{4} \quad \frac{1}{3} \quad \frac{1}{4} \quad \frac{1}{8} \quad \frac{1}{8}$$

_____

2. Which two numbers have a difference of $\frac{1}{8}$?

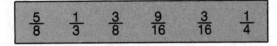

$$\frac{5}{8} \quad \frac{1}{3} \quad \frac{3}{8} \quad \frac{9}{16} \quad \frac{3}{16} \quad \frac{1}{4}$$

_____

3. Which two numbers have the sum that is closest to 1?

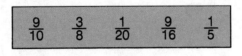

$$\frac{9}{10} \quad \frac{3}{8} \quad \frac{1}{20} \quad \frac{9}{16} \quad \frac{1}{5}$$

_____

4. Which two numbers have the difference that is closest to $\frac{1}{2}$?

$$\frac{7}{10} \quad \frac{3}{4} \quad \frac{1}{8} \quad \frac{9}{16} \quad \frac{1}{12}$$

_____

ADDING MIXED NUMBERS

WHAT'S FOR DINNER?

What's the best kind of pie to take on a picnic?

Write the answer to each problem. Then find each answer at the bottom. Write the letter for each problem on the line to answer the riddle.

P $3\frac{1}{5}$
$+\ 2\frac{3}{5}$

O $4\frac{1}{6}$
$+\ 3\frac{1}{12}$

H $12\frac{1}{3}$
$+\ 3\frac{2}{9}$

F $1\frac{3}{8}$
$+\ 1\frac{1}{4}$

Y $4\frac{2}{9}$
$+\ 1\frac{1}{3}$

S $9\frac{1}{5}$
$+\ 1\frac{3}{5}$

I $1\frac{11}{12}$
$+\ 4\frac{1}{4}$

E $1\frac{1}{6}$
$+\ 1\frac{1}{8}$

L $3\frac{1}{4} + 2\frac{1}{4} + 6\frac{1}{2}$

O $7\frac{9}{10} + 1\frac{1}{5} + 2\frac{1}{2}$

$10\frac{4}{5}$ $15\frac{5}{9}$ $11\frac{3}{5}$ $7\frac{1}{4}$

_____   _____   _____   _____

$2\frac{5}{8}$ 12 $5\frac{5}{9}$

_____   _____   _____

$5\frac{4}{5}$ $6\frac{1}{6}$ $2\frac{7}{24}$

_____   _____   _____

SUBTRACTING MIXED NUMBERS

PART MAGIC

Fill in the missing fractions in each magic square. The sum should be the same across, down, and on the diagonals of each square.

1.

$\frac{1}{12}$	$\frac{1}{6}$	$\frac{1}{4}$
$\frac{1}{12}$		

Magic Sum _____

2.

$\frac{3}{4}$		
0		
$\frac{3}{4}$		$\frac{1}{4}$

Magic Sum _____

3.

$\frac{4}{5}$		
	1	
$1\frac{3}{5}$		$1\frac{1}{5}$

Magic Sum _____

PROBLEM SOLVING

YOU BE THE TEACHER

Imagine that you are a teacher and that the problems below were solved by some of your students. Look at each problem. If the answer is correct, place a ✔ next to it. If the answer is incorrect, give the correct solution. Then explain the error so you can help your students to do better work. The first one is done for you.

1. Student A

$$
\begin{array}{r}
856 \\
723 \\
+\ 624 \\
\hline
\end{array}
$$
2,193 2,203

Error: _Did not regroup correctly._

2. Student B

$145.56 + 236.3 + 99.732 = 1,166.47$

Error: _____

_____

3. Student C

A box of paper plates costs $1.79 and a box of cups costs $0.79. How much change do you receive from $20 if you buy six boxes of plates and fives boxes of cups?

Error: _____ $5.31 _____

_____

4. Student D

A dozen pencils costs $2.79 and a dozen pens costs $5.95. How much more do 3 dozen pens cost than 2 dozen pencils?

Error: _____ $23.43 _____

_____

5. Student E

A box can hold 15 books. How many boxes will you need to pack 110 books?

Error: _____ 7 boxes _____

_____

_____

6. Student F

$6 \times (15 + 4) - 2 = 92$

Error: _____

_____

Name _____

MEASURING ANGLES

FINDING ALL THE ANGLES

Isn't this a logical idea? Suppose the numerals we use were shaped as follows: each numeral contained as many angles as the number is represented. For example, the numeral for "one" might be written this way so that it contained exactly one angle:

one angle

For each numeral below, number the angles. Show that each numeral contains the correct number of angles:

1.

2.

3.

4.

5.

6.

7.

8.

9. Can you figure out how the numeral for "nine" should be written?

PERPENDICULAR AND PARALLEL LINES

PERFECT MATCHES

What did the team call its young, impolite pitcher?

The two columns below contain a list of angles and line segments
from this figure. Draw a line from each angle or line segment on
the left to a congruent angle or line segment on the right. The
lines will cross through some of the letters. Write the remaining
letters at the bottom in the order they appear.

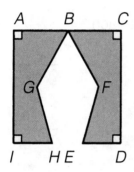

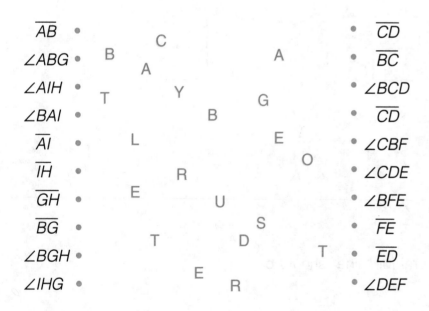

$\overline{AB}$ •

∠ABG •

∠AIH •

∠BAI •

$\overline{AI}$ •

$\overline{IH}$ •

$\overline{GH}$ •

$\overline{BG}$ •

∠BGH •

∠IHG •

• $\overline{CD}$

• $\overline{BC}$

• ∠BCD

• $\overline{CD}$

• ∠CBF

• ∠CDE

• ∠BFE

• $\overline{FE}$

• $\overline{ED}$

• ∠DEF

___ ___ ___ ___   ___ ___ ___ ___

COMPASS CONSTRUCTIONS

SEEING IS BELIEVING

1. Find and circle three triangles that are the same size and shape.

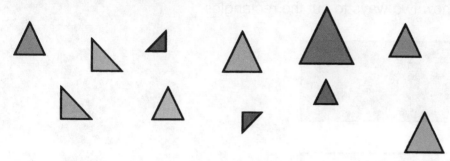

2. Find and circle two flags that have the same size poles and are pointing the same way.

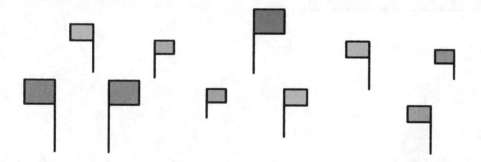

3. Find and circle two that are the same and in the same position.

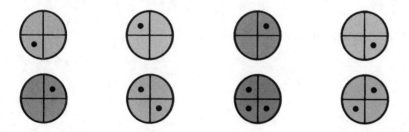

4. Find and circle two pairs that are the same shape but not the same size.

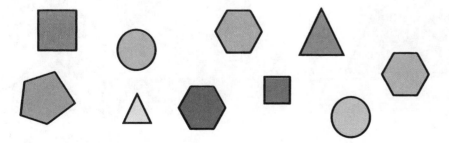

Name _____

QUADRILATERALS

CUTUPS

1. There are several ways to cut a rectangle into four congruent rectangles. Draw lines to show two ways to cut the rectangles.

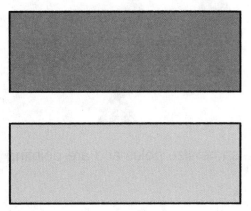

2. Draw lines to show how to divide this triangle into four congruent triangles.

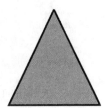

3. Draw lines to show how to divide this triangle into nine congruent triangles.

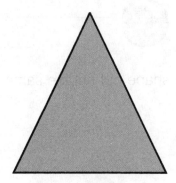

OTHER POLYGONS

COMBOS

There are three shapes on the left. Which of the figures on the right can be formed from the three shapes? The shapes can be moved or turned in any direction.

1. Figures: _____

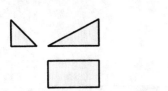

a.

b.

c.
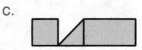

d.
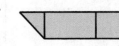

2. Figures: _____

a.

b.

c.
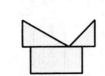

d.
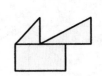

3. Figures: _____

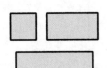

a.

b.
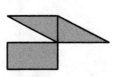

c.

d.

4. Figures: _____

a.

b.

c.

d.

RATIOS AND RATES

ME AND MY SHADOW

Here are some patterns where shadows are seen on a sidewalk square. Estimate the ratio of light area to shadow in each square. Write the ratio.

1.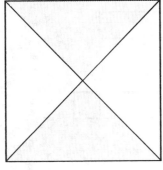

_____

2.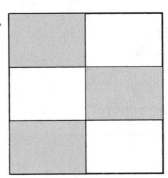

_____

3.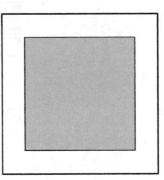

_____

4.

_____

5.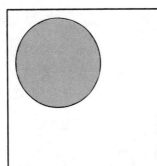

_____

6.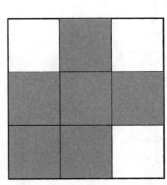

_____

7.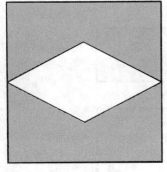

_____

8.

_____

9.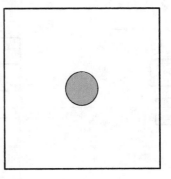

_____

Name _____

FINDING CIRCUMFERENCE

THE LONG WAY AROUND

What is the distance around each figure? Round your answers to
the nearest tenth.

1.

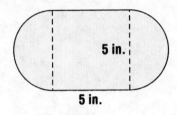

5 in.

5 in.

_____

2.

20 cm

_____

3.

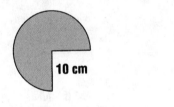

10 cm

_____

4.

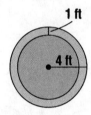

1 ft

4 ft

_____
(distance around
outer circle)

5.

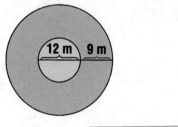

12 m   9 m

_____
(distance around
outer circle)

6.

4 in.   4 in.

4 in.

_____

7.

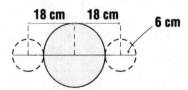

18 cm   18 cm   6 cm

_____
(distance around
all three circles)

8.

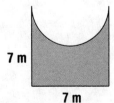

7 m

7 m

_____

Name _____

AREA OF A CIRCLE

CIRCULAR REASONING

What kind of circle does a truck driver like?

Find the area of each circle. Use a calculator to help you. Then find each answer on the wheel at the bottom. Write the letter for each answer on the wheel. Read around the circle to answer the question.

1. C

10 m

2. E

6 m

3. R

8 m

4. L

4.6 m

5. I

4 m

_____ _____ _____ _____ _____

6. E

5 m

7. S
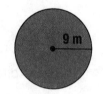
9 m

8. C

3.9 m

9. I

6.2 m

10. M
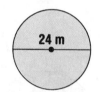
24 m

_____ _____ _____ _____

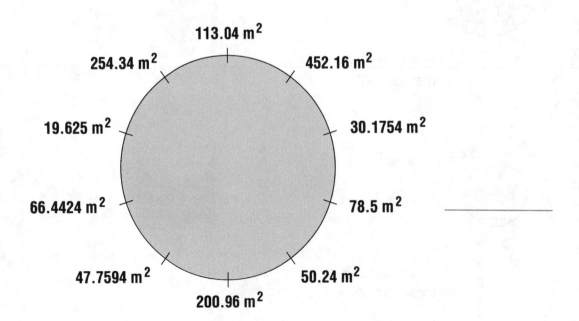

113.04 m^2

254.34 m^2 452.16 m^2

19.625 m^2 30.1754 m^2

66.4424 m^2 78.5 m^2

47.7594 m^2 50.24 m^2

200.96 m^2

_____

56

Name

DRAWING THREE-DIMENSIONAL FIGURES

KEEPING IT IN PERSPECTIVE

A. When you draw space figures, give a feeling of depth. Draw in **perspective.** As you look at a real object, like railroad tracks, for example, parallel lines *seem* to get closer in the distance. When you draw, instead of drawing lines parallel, make them get closer in the distance, too.

Here are some rules:

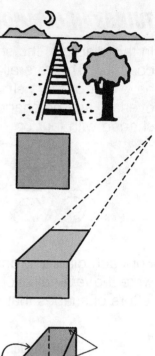

- Use parallel lines for any surface facing you, like the front of this prism.

- Make lines of surfaces that are receding (going away) from you slant towards each other slightly, like the top of this prism.

- Use the same slant for lines that go in the same direction, like these lines.

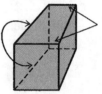

Complete these figures. Use perspective.

1. Rectangular prism   **2.** Triangular prism   **3.** Rectangular prism

B. Artists pick a point on their page and call it the vanishing point. All the receding parallel lines would meet at that point if they were extended far enough.

4. Draw a house in the space below. Pick a vanishing point. All receding parallel lines should meet at that point.

vanishing point

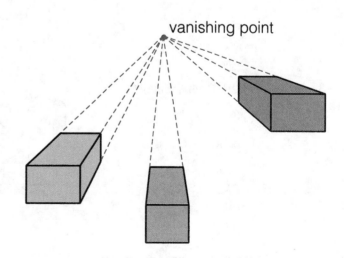

VOLUME OF A TRIANGULAR PRISM

THINGS IN COMMON

In this diagram, the shapes in the left circle all have something in common. They are all shaded. The shapes in the right circle all have four or more straight sides. In the middle, where the circles overlap, are the shapes which fit into both groups—they are shaded with four or more straight sides.

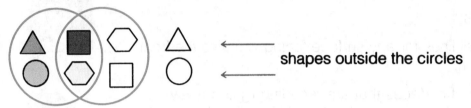

← ← shapes outside the circles

For each diagram, decide where each shape should go. Then write the *letter* of each shape in the correct place. Write the letters of shapes that do not belong in any circle outside the circles.

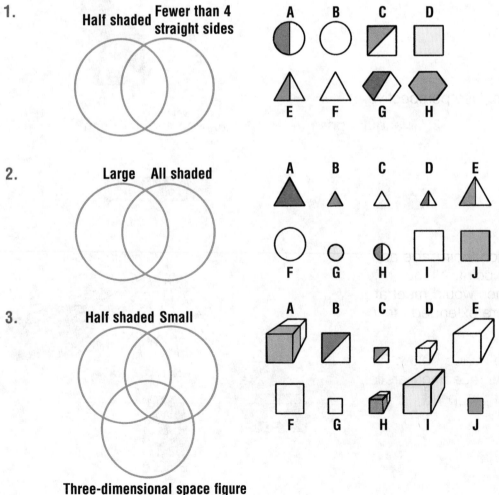

1.
Half shaded | Fewer than 4 straight sides

2.
Large | All shaded

3.
Half shaded | Small

Three-dimensional space figure

Name

VOLUME OF A CYLINDER

CUTOUTS

Part of each of these three-dimensional figures has been cut out.
Find the volume of the remainder.

Assume that when you see a shape cut out of one face of a
figure, that cut goes through the entire figure. So, if you see a
circle cut out of one side, the cutout figure is a cylinder.

1.

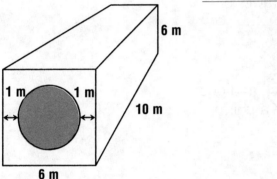

3.

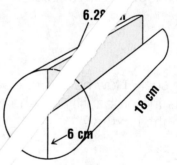

2.

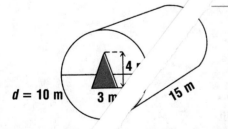

4.

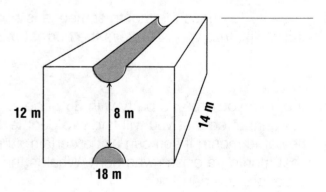

59

Probability

MIX AND MATCH

A. There are ten white socks and ten black socks in a drawer. Tony reaches into the drawer without looking.

1. What is the probability that he will pick a white sock?

   _____

2. What is the probability that he will pick a black sock?

   _____

3. Tony picks a white sock. Now he needs a match. What is the probability that he will pick a white sock from the drawer on the next try?

   _____

4. Tony picks a black sock. Now he has one white sock and one black sock. What is the probability that he will have a pair of matching socks on the next try?

   _____

5. Suppose the light is out so that Tony can't see the colors of the socks he picks. How many socks should he pick from the original 20 to be sure of getting at least one match?

   _____

B. Assume that an equal number of people are born in each month.

6. If you try to guess the month someone is born in, what is the probability that you will guess the correct month?

   _____

7. Suppose you are at a party with 35 people. You say that you can guarantee that you will find two people who were born in the same month if you can ask a certain number of people in what month he or she was born. What is the smallest number of people you can ask?

   _____

LOGIC STATEMENTS

TRUE BLUE

The words *all, some,* or *no (none)* can be used to tell how two groups are related. Consider the following sentences:

> All sparrows are birds.
> Some birds are sparrows.
> Some birds are not sparrows.
> No birds are fish.

Notice that a sparrow is always a bird, but a bird is not always a sparrow (for example, a bird may be a robin). A bird is never a fish.

Write *true* or *false* for each statement.

1. All dogs are mammals. _____

2. All mammals are dogs. _____

3. Some mammals are dogs. _____

4. No tables are mammals. _____

5. All squares are quadrilaterals. _____

6. Some quadrilaterals are not squares. _____

7. Some squares are not polygons. _____

8. All numbers greater than 40 are numbers greater than 30. _____

9. Some numbers greater than 30 are numbers greater than 40. _____

10. No even numbers are odd numbers. _____

11. No odd numbers are numbers greater than 40. _____

12. Some even numbers are not numbers that end in 0, 2, 4, 6, or 8. _____

PROBLEM SOLVING

IT WORKS LIKE MAGIC

In a magic square, the sum of each row, column, and diagonal is
the same. For example, here the sum is 150.

80	10	60
30	50	70
40	90	20

1. Look at the magic squares below. What do these squares
   and the one above have in common? (*Hint:* Think about
   simpler numbers.)

24	3	18
9	15	21
12	27	6

$2\frac{2}{3}$	$\frac{1}{3}$	$\frac{6}{3}$
1	$1\frac{2}{3}$	$2\frac{1}{3}$
$1\frac{1}{3}$	3	$\frac{2}{3}$

_____

_____

_____

2. Now use the same pattern to make two more magic squares.

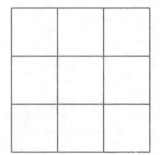

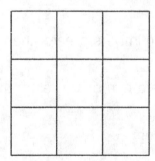

ANSWER KEY

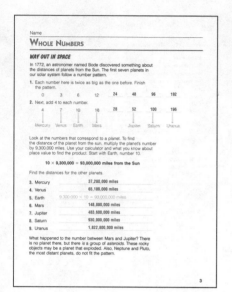

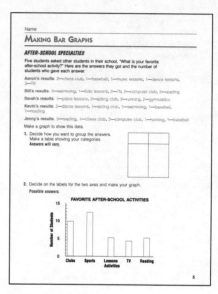

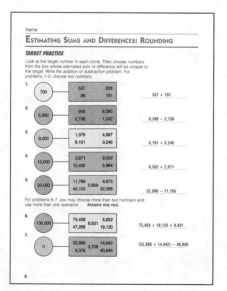

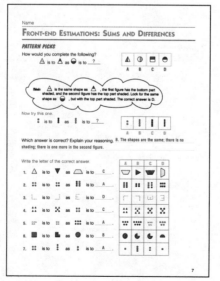

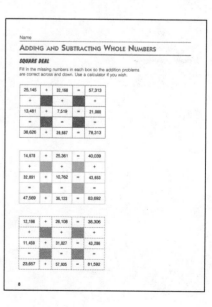

ANSWER KEY

Worksheet (page 9) — Solving Equations

Name

SOLVING EQUATIONS

EXTREME MEASURES

How do you measure poison ivy?

Solve each equation. Then draw a line to connect each pair of equations that have the same answer. (Use a ruler and draw a line between the dots.) The letters that are not crossed out will answer the riddle.

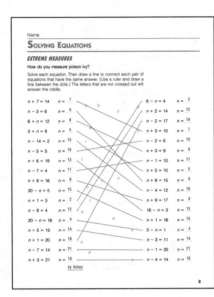

$n + 7 = 14$	$n = 7$		$6 - n = 4$	$n = 2$
$n - 3 = 6$	$n = 9$		$n + 2 = 14$	$n = 12$
$6 + n = 12$	$n = 6$		$n - 2 = 17$	$n = 19$
$3 + n = 8$	$n = 5$		$n + 3 = 10$	$n = 7$
$n - 14 = 2$	$n = 16$		$n + 3 = 10$	$n = 10$
$n - 5 = 5$	$n = 10$		$n + 3 = 9$	$n = 6$
$n + 6 = 19$	$n = 13$		$n - 1 = 10$	$n = 11$
$n - 7 = 4$	$n = 11$		$n + 5 = 10$	$n = 5$
$n + 8 = 16$	$n = 8$		$n + 6 = 15$	$n = 9$
$20 - n = 5$	$n = 15$		$n - 4 = 12$	$n = 16$
$n + 1 = 3$	$n = 2$		$n + 9 = 17$	$n = 8$
$n - 8 = 4$	$n = 12$		$n + 3 = 10$	$n = 13$
$20 - n = 16$	$n = 4$		$n + 1 = 16$	$n = 15$
$n + 5 = 19$	$n = 14$		$5 - n = 1$	$n = 4$
$n + 1 = 20$	$n = 19$		$n - 3 = 11$	$n = 14$
$n - 7 = 14$	$n = 21$		$n - 1 = 20$	$n = 21$
$n + 3 = 21$	$n = 18$		$n - 4 = 14$	$n = 18$

by itches

9

Worksheet (page 10) — Making Line Graphs

Name

MAKING LINE GRAPHS

COMMON QUALITIES

Here are two sets of numbers. Set A has odd numbers. Set B has even numbers.

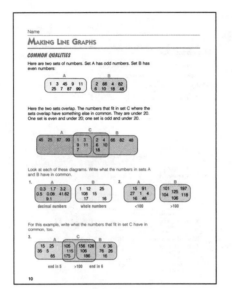

A	B
1 3 45 9 11	2 66 4 82
25 7 87 99	6 10 18 48

Here the two sets overlap. The numbers that fit in set C where the sets overlap have something else in common. They are under 20. One set is even and under 20; one set is odd and under 20.

A	C	B
45 25 87 99	1 3 / 2 4	66 82 48
	9 11 / 6	
	7 / 18	

Look at each of these diagrams. Write what the numbers in sets A and B have in common.

1.
A	B
0.3 1.7 3.2	1 12
0.5 0.08 41.62	108 15
9.1	17 16

decimal numbers   whole numbers

2.
A	B
15 91	101 197
27 1 4	125 118
16 46	104 106

<100   >100

For this example, write what the numbers that fit in set C have in common, too.

3.
A	C	B
15 25	105 156 126	6 36
35 5	115 106	76 26
65	175 186	16

end in 5   >100   end in 6

10

Worksheet (page 11) — Mental Math: Multiplying

Name

MENTAL MATH: MULTIPLYING

WHO'S WHO?

Anne, Beth, Charles, and David go to four different schools. The schools are Lincoln, Washington, Cleveland, and Roosevelt. Write the school that each student goes to. Use the clues below to help you.

Anne — Lincoln
Beth — Roosevelt
Charles — Cleveland
David — Washington

CLUES

1. The person who goes to Washington is a boy.
2. Charles used to go to Washington, but he changed schools this year.
3. Anne's school played softball against Roosevelt last month.
4. The student at Roosevelt is a girl.
5. Charles's cousin lives on the other side of town and goes to Lincoln.

You might find it helpful to fill in this chart as you get information about the students. Write X for no and ✓ for yes.

	Lincoln	Washington	Cleveland	Roosevelt
Anne	✓	x	x	x
Beth	x	x	x	✓
Charles	x	x	✓	x
David	x	✓	x	x

11

Worksheet (page 12) — Multiplying

Name

MULTIPLYING

SCRAMBLED NUMBERS

Use the numbers in the box to write the factors and the product for each multiplication problem.

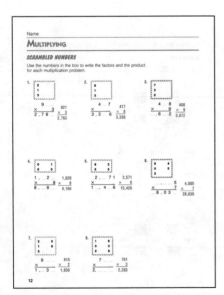

12

Worksheet (page 13) — Multiplying Greater Numbers

Name

MULTIPLYING GREATER NUMBERS

SERIOUS SERIES

These numbers follow a pattern. Each number is 12 times the number before it.

3   36   432   5,184

The next two numbers in the series are 62,208 (5,184 × 12) and 746,496 (62,208 × 12).

For each series, describe the pattern. Then fill in the next two numbers in each series. Use a calculator to help you. (Hint: Remember, not every series uses multiplication.)

1. 4 64 1,024 16,384 262,144   multiply by 16
2. 5 10 15 20 25 30 35   add 5
3. 3 51 867 14,739 250,563   multiply by 17
4. 23 184 1,472 11,776 94,208 753,664   multiply by 8
5. 3 8 40 45 225 230 1,150 1,155   add 5, multiply by 5
6. 6 13 91 98 686 693 4,851 4,858   add 7, multiply by 7
7. 12 10 660 658 43,428 43,426 2,866,116   subtract 2, multiply by 66
8. 10 90 81 729 720 6,480   subtract 9, multiply by 9
9. 124 248 496 992 1,984 3,968   multiply by 2
10. 375 75 600 300 2,400 2,100 16,800   subtract 300, multiply by 8

11. Write a series using a multiplication pattern. Give it to a friend to solve.
    Answers will vary.

12. Write a series with a pattern that uses addition or subtraction and multiplication. Give it to a friend to solve.
    Answers will vary.

13

Worksheet (page 14) — Exponents

Name

EXPONENTS

EXPONENTIALLY SPEAKING

Remember that you can use exponents to show multiplication when all the factors are the same.

$$5 \times 5 \times 5 \times 5 = 5^4$$

Now study the multiplication shown below.

$$(3 \times 3 \times 3) \times (3 \times 3) = 3 \times 3 \times 3 \times 3 \times 3$$
$$27 \times 9 = 243$$

Write the exponents and the product in each problem. Then check that the products are correct. Use a calculator.

1.
$$3 \times 3 \times 3 = 3^3$$
$$\times \quad 3 \times 3 = \times 3^2 = \times 2\,7$$
$$3 \times 3 \times 3 \times 3 \times 3 = 3^5 = 2\,4\,3$$

2.
$$4 \times 4 \times 4 \times 4 = 4^4$$
$$\times \quad 4 \times 4 = \times 4^2 = \times 1\,6$$
$$4 \times 4 \times 4 \times 4 \times 4 \times 4 = 4^6 = 4\,0\,9\,6$$

3.
$$2 \times 2 \times 2 = 2^3$$
$$\times \quad 2 \times 2 \times 2 = \times 2^3 = \times 8$$
$$2 \times 2 \times 2 \times 2 \times 2 \times 2 = 2^6 = 6\,4$$

4. Can you write a rule that tells how to multiply two or more numbers in exponent form? What must be true about the base of each exponential number?
   The bases must be the same. To multiply, use the same base and add the exponents of the numbers.

Use your rule to write the answer to these problems. Then write the factors and products in standard form. Check that the products are correct. Use a calculator.

5. $4^2 \times 4^2 = 4^4$ — $16 \times 16 = 256$
6. $7^4 \times 7^3 = 7^7$ — $2,401 \times 343 = 823,543$
7. $12^3 \times 12^2 = 12^5$ — $1,728 \times 144 = 248,832$
8. $2^3 \times 2^3 \times 2^4 = 2^8$ — $4 \times 8 \times 16 = 512$

14

ANSWER KEY

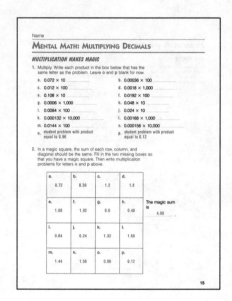

MENTAL MATH: MULTIPLYING DECIMALS

MULTIPLICATION MAKES MAGIC

1. Multiply. Write each product in the box below that has the same letter as the problem. Leave o and p blank for now.

a. 0.072 × 10   b. 0.00036 × 100
c. 0.012 × 100   d. 0.0018 × 1,000
e. 0.108 × 10   f. 0.0192 × 100
g. 0.0006 × 1,000   h. 0.048 × 10
i. 0.0084 × 100   j. 0.024 × 10
k. 0.000132 × 10,000   l. 0.00168 × 1,000
m. 0.0144 × 100   n. 0.000156 × 10,000
o. student problem with product   p. student problem with product
   equal to 0.96   equal to 0.12

2. In a magic square, the sum of each row, column, and diagonal should be the same. Fill in the two missing boxes so that you have a magic square. Then write multiplication problems for letters o and p above.

a. 0.72	b. 0.36	c. 1.2	d. 1.8
e. 1.08	f. 1.92	g. 0.6	h. 0.48
i. 0.84	j. 0.24	k. 1.32	l. 1.68
m. 1.44	n. 1.56	o. 0.96	p. 0.12

The magic sum is 4.86

15

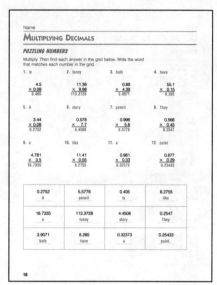

MULTIPLYING DECIMALS

PUZZLING NUMBERS

Multiply. Then find each answer in the grid below. Write the word that matches each number in the grid.

1. is
   4.5
   × 0.09
   0.405

2. funny
   11.36
   × 9.98
   113.3728

3. both
   0.89
   × 4.39
   3.9071

4. have
   55.1
   × 0.15
   8.265

5. A
   3.44
   × 0.08
   0.2752

6. story
   0.578
   × 7.7
   4.4506

7. pencil
   0.996
   × 5.6
   5.5776

8. They
   0.566
   × 0.45
   0.2547

9. a
   4.781
   × 3.5
   16.7335

10. like
    11.41
    × 0.55
    6.2755

11. a
    0.981
    × 0.33
    0.32373

12. point
    0.877
    × 0.29
    0.25433

0.2752 A	5.5776 pencil	0.405 is	6.2755 like
16.7335 a	113.3728 funny	4.4506 story.	0.2547 They
3.9071 both	8.265 have	0.32373 a	0.25433 point.

16

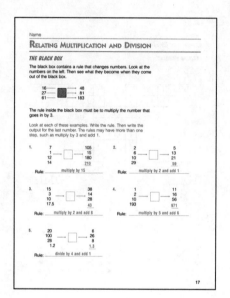

RELATING MULTIPLICATION AND DIVISION

THE BLACK BOX

The black box contains a rule that changes numbers. Look at the numbers on the left. Then see what they become when they come out of the black box.

16 → 48
27 → 81
61 → 183

The rule inside the black box must be to multiply the number that goes in by 3.

Look at each of these examples. Write the rule. Then write the output for the last number. The rules may have more than one step, such as multiply by 3 and add 1.

1. 7 → 105
   1 → 15
   12 → 180
   14 → 210
   Rule: multiply by 15

2. 2 → 5
   6 → 13
   10 → 21
   29 → 59
   Rule: multiply by 2 and add 1

3. 15 → 38
   3 → 14
   10 → 28
   17.5 → 43
   Rule: multiply by 2 and add 8

4. 1 → 11
   10 → 56
   193 → 971
   Rule: multiply by 5 and add 6

5. 20 → 6
   100 → 26
   28 → 8
   1.2 → 1.3
   Rule: divide by 4 and add 1

17

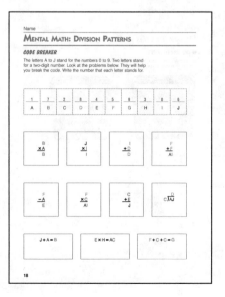

MENTAL MATH: DIVISION PATTERNS

CODE BREAKER

The letters A to J stand for the numbers 0 to 9. Two letters stand for a two-digit number. Look at the problems below. They will help you break the code. Write the number that each letter stands for.

1	7	2	6	3	9	5	4	8	0
A	B	C	D	E	F	G	H	I	J

B   J   I   F
×A   ×I   +D   +F
B   I   D   AI

F   F   C   D
−A   ×C   +E   C)AJ
E   AI   J

J + A = B   E × H = AC   F + C + C = G

18

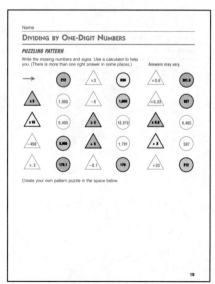

DIVIDING BY ONE-DIGIT NUMBERS

PUZZLING PATTERN

Write the missing numbers and signs. Use a calculator to help you. (There is more than one right answer in some places.)

Answers may vary.

Create your own pattern puzzle in the space below.

19

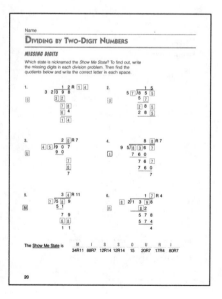

DIVIDING BY TWO-DIGIT NUMBERS

MISSING DIGITS

Which state is nicknamed the *Show Me State*? To find out, write the missing digits in each division problem. Then find the quotients below and write the correct letter in each space.

The Show Me State is   M I S S O U R I
                       34R11 88R7 12R14 12R14 15 20R7 17R4 80R7

20

ANSWER KEY

PUZZLING NUMBERS

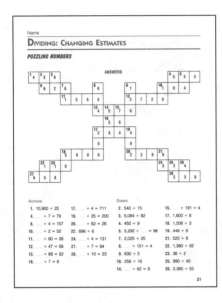

ANSWERS

Across
1. 10,900 ÷ 25
4. ___ ÷ 79 = 79
6. ___ + 4 = 157
10. ___ ÷ 2 = 52
11. ___ + 60 = 26
12. ___ + 47 = 58
13. ___ + 88 = 52
16. ___ + 7 = 8
17. ___ + 4 = 711
19. ___ + 25 = 200
20. ___ + 82 = 28
24. ___ + 4 = 131
27. ___ + 7 = 94
28. ___ + 10 = 23

Down
2. 540 ÷ 15
3. 5,084 ÷ 82
4. 450 ÷ 9
5. 5,292 ÷ ___ = 98
7. 2,025 ÷ 25
8. ___ + 151 = 4
9. 630 ÷ 5
10. 256 ÷ 16
14. ___ + 62 = 9
15. ___ ÷ 191 = 4
17. 1,600 ÷ 8
18. 1,206 ÷ 3
19. 448 ÷ 8
21. 520 ÷ 8
22. 1,380 ÷ 92
23. 36 ÷ 2
25. 990 ÷ 45
26. 2,365 ÷ 55

21

SQUARE OFF

Use these numbers to fill in the square so that the division problems are correct across each row and down each column. One row is already filled in for you.

952   68   8,092   238   64,736   34

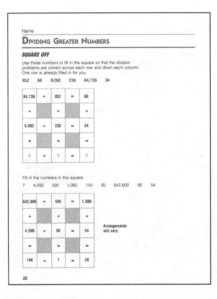

Fill in the numbers in this square.

7   4,590   595   1,080   140   20   642,600   85   54

Arrangements will vary.

22

DEEP DEPTHS

Mt. Everest is the highest point on the earth. What is the lowest point? To find out, solve each equation. Write the letter above each question in the space below that matches n. (Write the letter everywhere there is a matching number.)

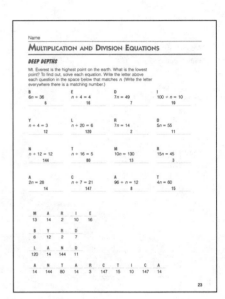

B	E	D	I
6n = 36	n + 4 = 4	7n = 49	100 ÷ n = 10
6	16	7	10

Y	L	R	D
n ÷ 4 = 3	n + 20 = 6	7n = 14	5n = 55
12	120	2	11

N	T	M	R
n + 12 = 12	n + 16 = 5	10n = 130	15n = 45
144	80	13	3

A	C	A	T
2n = 28	n + 7 = 21	96 ÷ n = 12	4n = 60
14	147	8	15

M A R I E
13 14 2 10 16

B Y R D
6 12 2 7

L A N D
120 14 144 11

A N T A R C T I C A
14 144 80 14 3 147 15 10 147 14

23

A SHRINKING VIOLET?

What gets shorter as it grows older?

Divide mentally. Then arrange the answers from least to greatest on the lines below. Write the letter for each problem above it. You'll have the answer to the riddle.

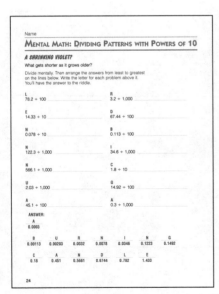

L
78.2 ÷ 100

E
14.33 ÷ 10

N
0.078 ÷ 10

N
122.3 ÷ 1,000

N
566.1 ÷ 1,000

U
2.03 ÷ 1,000

A
45.1 ÷ 100

R
3.2 ÷ 1,000

D
67.44 ÷ 100

B
0.113 ÷ 100

I
34.6 ÷ 1,000

C
1.8 ÷ 10

G
14.92 ÷ 100

A
0.3 ÷ 1,000

ANSWER:
A
0.0003

B   U   R   N   I   N   G
0.00113 0.00203 0.0032   0.0078   0.0346   0.1223   0.1492

C   A   N   D   L   E
0.18   0.451   0.5681 0.6744 0.782   1.433

24

ZEROED OUT

Fill in the missing numbers in these division problems.

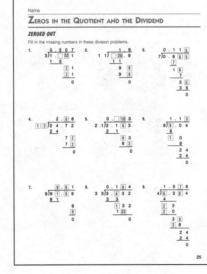

25

IF THE NUMBER FITS

For each problem, pick a divisor and quotient from the baskets to make a correct division problem. Use each number exactly once.

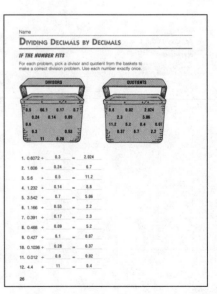

DIVISORS
0.5   56.1   0.17   0.7
0.24 0.14   0.09
0.6   0.53
    11   0.28

QUOTIENTS
8.8   0.02   2.024
2.3   5.06
11.2 5.2   0.4   0.07
    0.37   6.7

1. 0.6072 ÷ 0.3 = 2.024
2. 1.608 ÷ 0.24 = 6.7
3. 5.6 ÷ 0.5 = 11.2
4. 1.232 ÷ 0.14 = 8.8
5. 3.542 ÷ 0.7 = 5.06
6. 1.166 ÷ 0.53 = 2.2
7. 0.391 ÷ 0.17 = 2.3
8. 0.468 ÷ 0.09 = 5.2
9. 0.427 ÷ 6.1 = 0.07
10. 0.1036 ÷ 0.28 = 0.37
11. 0.012 ÷ 0.6 = 0.02
12. 4.4 ÷ 11 = 0.4

26

68

ANSWER KEY

ROUNDING DECIMAL QUOTIENTS

UNCOVER THE FACTS

What baseball player's record for the most home runs lasted from 1935 to 1974?

To find the facts, use your ruler to connect the problems on the left with the answers on the right. Round to the nearest place indicated in parentheses. Use your calculator.

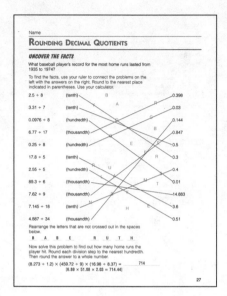

2.5 ÷ 8	(tenth)	.0.398
3.31 ÷ 7		.0.03
0.0976 ÷ 8	(hundredth)	.0.144
6.77 ÷ 17	(thousandth)	.0.847
0.25 ÷ 8	(hundredth)	.0.5
17.8 ÷ 5	(tenth)	.0.3
2.55 ÷ 5	(hundredth)	.0.4
89.3 ÷ 6	(thousandth)	.0.01
7.62 ÷ 9	(thousandth)	.14.883
7.145 ÷ 18	(tenth)	.3.6
4.887 ÷ 34	(thousandth)	.0.51

Rearrange the letters that are not crossed out in the spaces below.

B A B E   R U T H

Now solve this problem to find out how many home runs the player hit. Round each division step to the nearest hundredth. Then round the answer to a whole number.

(8.273 ÷ 1.2) × (459.72 ÷ 9) × (16.96 ÷ 8.37) = ____ 714
[6.89 × 51.08 × 2.03 = 714.44]

27

ORDER OF OPERATIONS

FIGURE IT OUT

In the pattern below, there are two sets of figures. In each set, the figures are related in the same way. The second figure is a smaller version of the first.

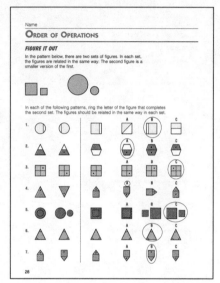

In each of the following patterns, ring the letter of the figure that completes the second set. The figures should be related in the same way in each set.

28

MEAN, MEDIAN, MODE, AND RANGE

MAKE THE GRADE

Imagine that you are teacher for a day. Here are your students' scores on a math test. There are a possible 100 points on the test. What grade will you give each student?

In order to be fair, you should use some statistics to help you. You can calculate the mean, mode, median, and range of the scores. Make up a scale telling what scores get a passing grade (A, B, C, or D) and what scores fail (F).

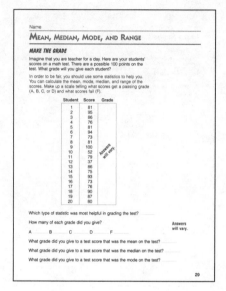

Student	Score	Grade
1	81	
2	95	
3	86	
4	76	
5	81	
6	94	
7	73	
8	81	
9	100	
10	52	Answers will vary
11	79	
12	37	
13	86	
14	75	
15	93	
16	73	
17	76	
18	90	
19	87	
20	80	

Which type of statistic was most helpful in grading the test?

How many of each grade did you give?

A ____ B ____ C ____ D ____ F ____   Answers will vary.

What grade did you give to a test score that was the mean on the test?

What grade did you give to a test score that was the median on the test?

What grade did you give to a test score that was the mode on the test?

29

FACTORS AND GREATEST COMMON FACTOR

DAFFY DINO DEFINITION

Which dinosaur was the fastest?

Using a ruler, draw a line from the numbers on the left to their greatest common factor (GCF) on the right. The letters that remain will answer the question. Write the letters in order, reading from top to bottom, in the blank below.

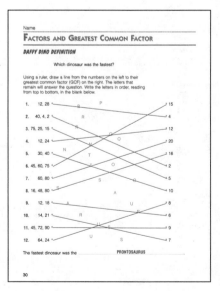

1. 12, 28		15
2. 40, 4, 2		4
3. 75, 25, 15		12
4. 12, 24		20
5. 30, 40		16
6. 45, 60, 75		2
7. 60, 80		5
8. 16, 48, 80		10
9. 12, 18		8
10. 14, 21		6
11. 45, 72, 90		9
12. 64, 24		7

The fastest dinosaur was the ____ PRONTOSAURUS

30

MULTIPLES AND LEAST COMMON MULTIPLE

CAREFUL ARRANGEMENTS

How can you arrange four 3s so the value is 36? Here is one way:

(3 + 3) × (3 + 3) → 6 × 6 = 36

In the puzzles below, you can use any operation signs you choose, as well as decimal points or fractions. **Answers will vary.**

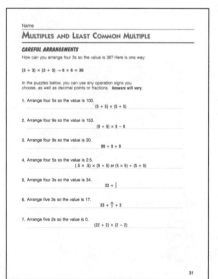

1. Arrange four 5s so the value is 100.
   (5 + 5) × (5 + 5)

2. Arrange four 9s so the value is 153.
   (9 + 9) × 9 − 9

3. Arrange four 9s so the value is 20.
   99 ÷ 9 + 9

4. Arrange four 5s so the value is 2.5.
   (.5 × .5) × (5 + 5) or (5 × 5) ÷ (5 + 5)

5. Arrange four 3s so the value is 34.
   33 + 3/3

6. Arrange five 3s so the value is 17.
   33 ÷ 3 + 3 + 3

7. Arrange five 2s so the value is 0.
   (22 + 2) × (2 − 2)

31

FRACTIONS AND EQUIVALENT FRACTIONS

FRACTURED FAIRY TALE

What fairy tale is about some talking vegetables?

Write an equivalent fraction for each of the following fractions. Then find the answers under the lines below. Write the letter for each fraction on the line. The first letter has been filled in.

J A C K
5/10   2/4   1/3

A N D
10/12   1/5   1/2

T H E
1/8   18/20   1/6

B E A N S
6/8   4/5   1/4   11/10

T A L K
1/7   10/10   10/20   4/5

32

69

ANSWER KEY

Name

MIXED NUMBERS

CURIOUS CODE

In each problem, the numbers have been replaced by letters. Each letter always stands for the same number. It may be a 1-digit number or a 2-digit number. All answers are fractions or mixed numbers written in simplest terms.

Use the clue and logic to decide what number each letter stands for. Write the 12 letters and numbers on the lines below.

CLUE: L = 2

$\frac{L}{F} = \frac{S}{L}$ $\frac{A}{F} = S\frac{S}{F}$ $\frac{E}{A} = S\frac{F}{A}$

$\frac{I}{E} = \frac{S}{I}$ $\frac{O}{F} = L\frac{I}{F}$ $\frac{H}{L} = L\frac{S}{I}$

$\frac{C}{F} = I$ $\frac{T}{C} = \frac{S}{L}$ $\frac{B}{T} = S\frac{S}{I}$

$\frac{Y}{F} = L\frac{S}{L}$

Letter	Number	Letter	Number
L	2	O	11
S	1	H	7
F	4	C	12
A	5	T	6
E	8	B	9
I	3	Y	10

Now replace each number with its corresponding letter to get the answer to this riddle:

"How is a frog like a baseball player?"

T h e y   b o t h   c a t c h

f l i e s

33

Name

COMPARING AND ORDERING

DAFFYNITIONS

To answer each riddle, write each group of fractions and mixed numbers in order from least to greatest. Write the letter of each number below the line.

What do you call the place where school lunches are made?

O	U	R	S	O	H	M	M
$\frac{1}{6}$	$\frac{5}{7}$	$\frac{7}{9}$	$\frac{1}{12}$	$\frac{5}{6}$	$1\frac{1}{4}$	$1\frac{2}{3}$	$1\frac{5}{6}$
m	u	s	h	r	o	o	m

What do you call a twisted doughnut?

T	P	L	E	Z	E	R
$\frac{7}{12}$	$\frac{3}{4}$	$1\frac{1}{6}$	$\frac{1}{2}$	$1\frac{5}{12}$	$\frac{11}{12}$	$1\frac{1}{2}$
p	r	e	t	z	e	l

What do you call a cucumber in a sour mood?

I	L	K	P	C	E
$\frac{3}{16}$	$\frac{3}{4}$	$\frac{7}{16}$	$\frac{3}{32}$	$\frac{5}{8}$	$\frac{7}{16}$
p	i	c	k	l	e

What do you call a song played on an automobile radio?

R	C	A	O	O	N	T
$1\frac{7}{8}$	$1\frac{1}{6}$	$1\frac{1}{3}$	$1\frac{1}{2}$	$1\frac{2}{3}$	$1\frac{5}{8}$	$1\frac{11}{12}$
c	a	r	t	o	o	n

34

Name

ROUNDING FRACTIONS AND MIXED NUMBERS

FRACTION ACTION

You can use mental math to decide if a fraction is greater than $\frac{1}{2}$.

Example: Is $\frac{3}{5} > \frac{1}{2}$?

Double the numerator. $2 \times 3 = 6$

If the result is greater than the denominator, $6 > 5$

the fraction is greater than $\frac{1}{2}$.   so $\frac{3}{5} > \frac{1}{2}$

Is the fraction greater than $\frac{1}{2}$? Write YES or NO.

1. $\frac{4}{5}$ YES   2. $\frac{2}{7}$ NO   3. $\frac{5}{11}$ NO   4. $\frac{7}{16}$ NO

5. $\frac{7}{10}$ YES   6. $\frac{8}{17}$ NO   7. $\frac{10}{19}$ YES

In the maze below, find a path from START to END. Use only fractions that are greater than $\frac{1}{2}$. You may go up, down, across, or diagonally, but do not cross a number more than once.

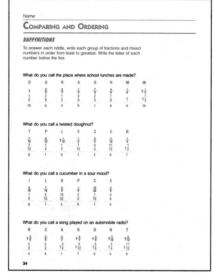

35

Name

CUSTOMARY UNITS OF LENGTH

GOING TO GREAT LENGTH

Arrange these items from longest to shortest. (You'll have to find a way to compare their lengths first, since they are all given in different units.)

Remember, a mile is 5,280 feet.

White Sea—Baltic Canal, Soviet Union	141 mi
Golden Gate Bridge, California	1,400 yd
Simplon I Tunnel, Switzerland to Italy	12.3 mi
Sydney Harbor Bridge, Australia	19,800 in.
Panama Canal, Panama	50.7 mi
Mackinac Straits Bridge, Michigan	45,600 in.
Verrazano Narrows Bridge, New York	4,260 ft
Welland Canal, Canada	49,280 yd
Suez Canal, Egypt	100.6 mi
New River Gorge Bridge, West Virginia	1,700 ft
Rokko Tunnel, Japan	633,600 in.
Northern Line Subway Tunnel, England	30,488 yd

1.	White Sea–Baltic Canal, Soviet Union	141 mi
2.	Suez Canal, Egypt	100.6 mi
3.	Panama Canal, Panama	50.7 mi
4.	Welland Canal, Canada	49,280 yd
5.	Northern Line Subway Tunnel, England	30,488 yd
6.	Simplon I Tunnel, Switzerland to Italy	12.3 mi
7.	Rokko Tunnel, Japan	633,600 in.
8.	Verrazano Narrows Bridge, New York	4,260 ft
9.	Golden Gate Bridge, California	1,400 yd
10.	Mackinac Straits Bridge, Michigan	45,600 in.
11.	New River Gorge Bridge, West Virginia	1,700 ft
12.	Sydney Harbor Bridge, Australia	19,800 in.

36

Name

FRACTIONS, MIXED NUMBERS, AND DECIMALS

CROSSHATCH

Try to find a decimal in columns 3 and 4 that matches each fraction or mixed number in columns 1 and 2. When you find a match, cross out both the numbers and the letters next to them. A match may be found in any row. An example is done for you.

COLUMN 1	COLUMN 2	COLUMN 3	COLUMN 4
C ~~$1\frac{1}{10}$~~	A ~~$\frac{4}{5}$~~	U 0.34	A ~~0.8~~
E $\frac{75}{1000}$	P $4\frac{89}{100}$	E 6.25	T 0.11
O ~~$\frac{3}{4}$~~	E ~~$\frac{1}{4}$~~	B ~~0.25~~	O ~~1.1~~
T $\frac{3}{5}$	I $7\frac{99}{1000}$	E ~~0.75~~	A 4.089
B ~~$\frac{1}{1000}$~~	R ~~$6\frac{1}{4}$~~	Q 9.855	E ~~2.005~~
T $\frac{5}{8}$	I ~~$\frac{1}{4}$~~	N ~~6.125~~	E 9.12
N $\frac{18}{25}$	N ~~$9\frac{1}{8}$~~	A 7.099	S 7.5
E ~~$\frac{2}{5}$~~	O $\frac{80}{1000}$	M ~~0.4~~	T ~~1.25~~
H $3\frac{1}{100}$	T $\frac{7}{10}$	L 1.02	L 2.8

Now write the letters that are left in each column on the line. Unscramble each group of letters to spell a familiar mathematical word.

COLUMN 1	ETTNH	TENTH
COLUMN 2	PINOT	POINT
COLUMN 3	UEQAL	EQUAL
COLUMN 4	TAESL	LEAST

37

Name

ADDING FRACTIONS: UNLIKE DENOMINATORS

THE MISSING LINK

Fill in the boxes with the missing numbers. Each fraction in these problems should be in its simplest form.

1. $\frac{1}{2}$
    $+\frac{1}{4}$
    ___
    $\frac{3}{4}$

2. $\frac{1}{3}$
    $+\frac{1}{3}$
    ___
    $\frac{2}{3}$

3. $\frac{1}{4}$
    $+\frac{1}{4}$
    ___
    $\frac{1}{2}$

4. $\frac{5}{16}$
    $+\frac{3}{16}$
    ___
    $\frac{7}{12}$

5. $\frac{1}{3}$
    $+\frac{1}{4}$
    ___
    $\frac{7}{12}$

6. $\frac{3}{8}$
    $+\frac{5}{8}$
    ___
    $1\frac{1}{8}$

7. $\frac{3}{10}$
    $+\frac{9}{10}$
    ___
    $1\frac{1}{5}$

8. $\frac{3}{8}$
    $+\frac{5}{8}$
    ___
    $1\frac{3}{8}$

38

ANSWER KEY

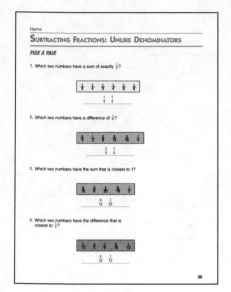

Name

SUBTRACTING FRACTIONS: UNLIKE DENOMINATORS

PICK A PAIR

1. Which two numbers have a sum of exactly $\frac{1}{2}$?

$\frac{1}{4} \quad \frac{1}{4}$

2. Which two numbers have a difference of $\frac{1}{2}$?

$\frac{3}{8} \quad \frac{1}{4}$

3. Which two numbers have the sum that is closest to 1?

$\frac{9}{10} \quad \frac{1}{20}$

4. Which two numbers have the difference that is closest to $\frac{1}{2}$?

$\frac{9}{10} \quad \frac{1}{12}$

39

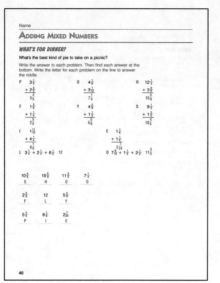

Name

ADDING MIXED NUMBERS

WHAT'S FOR DINNER?

What's the best kind of pie to take on a picnic?

Write the answer to each problem. Then find each answer at the bottom. Write the letter for each problem on the line to answer the riddle.

$$P \quad 3\frac{1}{3} \\ +\ 2\frac{1}{3} \\ \overline{5\frac{4}{5}}$$

$$O \quad 4\frac{1}{4} \\ +\ 3\frac{3}{12} \\ \overline{7\frac{1}{4}}$$

$$H \quad 12\frac{1}{2} \\ +\ 3\frac{1}{3} \\ \overline{15\frac{5}{6}}$$

$$F \quad 1\frac{3}{4} \\ +\ 1\frac{1}{3} \\ \overline{2\frac{5}{9}}$$

$$Y \quad 4\frac{2}{3} \\ +\ 1\frac{1}{3} \\ \overline{5\frac{3}{5}}$$

$$S \quad 9\frac{1}{4} \\ +\ 1\frac{3}{4} \\ \overline{10\frac{5}{8}}$$

$$I \quad 1\frac{11}{12} \\ +\ 4\frac{1}{2} \\ \overline{6\frac{5}{6}}$$

$$E \quad 1\frac{1}{4} \\ +\ 1\frac{1}{3} \\ \overline{2\frac{7}{24}}$$

$$L \quad 3\frac{1}{4} + 2\frac{1}{2} + 6\frac{1}{4} \quad 12$$

$$O \quad 7\frac{5}{8} + 1\frac{1}{2} + 2\frac{1}{4} \quad 11\frac{3}{8}$$

$10\frac{1}{2}$	$15\frac{5}{8}$	$11\frac{3}{8}$	$7\frac{1}{4}$
S	H	O	O

$2\frac{1}{3}$	12	$5\frac{3}{5}$
F	L	Y

$5\frac{1}{3}$	$6\frac{1}{4}$	$2\frac{7}{24}$
P	I	E

40

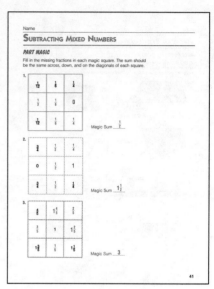

Name

SUBTRACTING MIXED NUMBERS

PART MAGIC

Fill in the missing fractions in each magic square. The sum should be the same across, down, and on the diagonals of each square.

1.

$\frac{1}{12}$	$\frac{1}{6}$	$\frac{1}{4}$
$\frac{1}{3}$	$\frac{1}{6}$	0
$\frac{1}{12}$	$\frac{1}{6}$	$\frac{1}{4}$

Magic Sum $\frac{1}{2}$

2.

$\frac{3}{4}$	$\frac{1}{4}$	$\frac{1}{2}$
0	$\frac{1}{2}$	1
$\frac{3}{4}$	$\frac{1}{2}$	$\frac{1}{4}$

Magic Sum $1\frac{1}{2}$

3.

$\frac{4}{5}$	$1\frac{3}{5}$	$\frac{3}{5}$
$\frac{3}{5}$	1	$1\frac{2}{5}$
$1\frac{3}{5}$	$\frac{1}{5}$	$1\frac{1}{5}$

Magic Sum 3

41

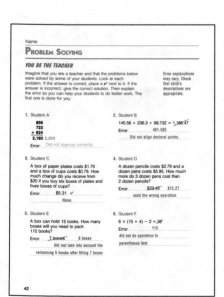

Name

PROBLEM SOLVING

YOU BE THE TEACHER

Imagine that you are a teacher and that the problems below were solved by some of your students. Look at each problem. If the answer is correct, place a ✓ next to it. If the answer is incorrect, give the correct solution. Then explain the error so you can help your students to do better work. The first one is done for you:

Error explanations may vary. Check that child's descriptions are appropriate.

1. Student A

$$\begin{array}{r} 856 \\ 723 \\ +\ 624 \\ \hline 2,193 \quad 2,203 \end{array}$$

Error: ___Did not regroup correctly.___

2. Student B

$$145.56 + 236.3 + 99.732 = 1,166.47$$

Error: ___481.592___

___Did not align decimal points.___

3. Student C

A box of paper plates costs $1.79 and a box of cups costs $0.79. How much change do you receive from $20 if you buy six boxes of plates and fives boxes of cups?

Error: ___$5.31 ✓___

___None.___

4. Student D

A dozen pencils costs $2.79 and a dozen pens costs $5.95. How much more do 3 dozen pens cost than 2 dozen pencils?

Error: ___$23.43___   ___$12.27___

___used the wrong operation___

5. Student E

A box can hold 15 books. How many boxes will you need to pack 110 books?

Error: ___7 boxes___   ___8 boxes___

___did not take into account the remaining 5 books after filling 7 boxes___

6. Student F

$$6 \times (15 + 4) - 2 = 92$$

Error: ___112___

___did not do operation in parentheses first___

42

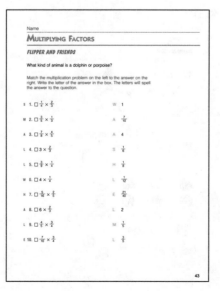

Name

MULTIPLYING FACTORS

FLIPPER AND FRIENDS

What kind of animal is a dolphin or porpoise?

Match the multiplication problem on the left to the answer on the right. Write the letter of the answer in the box. The letters will spell the answer to the question.

S 1. ☐ $\frac{1}{4} \times \frac{2}{5}$ W 1

M 2. ☐ $\frac{2}{5} \times \frac{1}{3}$ A $\frac{7}{10}$

A 3. ☐ $\frac{7}{8} \times \frac{4}{5}$ A 4

L 4. ☐ $3 \times \frac{2}{3}$ S $\frac{1}{8}$

L 5. ☐ $\frac{3}{4} \times \frac{1}{4}$ H $\frac{1}{10}$

W 6. ☐ $4 \times \frac{1}{4}$ L $\frac{1}{15}$

H 7. ☐ $\frac{5}{8} \times \frac{2}{5}$ E $\frac{2}{40}$

A 8. ☐ $6 \times \frac{2}{3}$ L 2

L 9. ☐ $\frac{4}{5} \times \frac{3}{4}$ M $\frac{1}{5}$

E 10. ☐ $\frac{7}{10} \times \frac{3}{4}$ L $\frac{3}{5}$

43

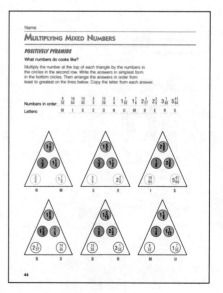

Name

MULTIPLYING MIXED NUMBERS

POSITIVELY PYRAMIDS

What numbers do cooks like?

Multiply the number at the top of each triangle by the numbers in the circles in the second row. Write the answers in simplest form in the bottom circles. Then arrange the answers in order from least to greatest on the lines below. Copy the letter from each answer.

Numbers in order: $\frac{9}{32}$ $\frac{19}{64}$ $\frac{14}{45}$ $\frac{3}{5}$ $\frac{3}{20}$ $\frac{1}{4}$ $1\frac{1}{32}$ $1\frac{7}{8}$ $2\frac{2}{27}$ $2\frac{2}{5}$ $3\frac{1}{10}$ $6\frac{41}{64}$

Letters: M   I   X   E   D   N   U   M   B   E   R   S

44

71

ANSWER KEY

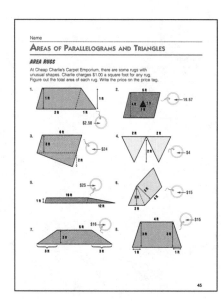

AREAS OF PARALLELOGRAMS AND TRIANGLES

AREA RUGS

At Cheap Charlie's Carpet Emporium, there are some rugs with unusual shapes. Charlie charges $1.00 a square foot for any rug. Figure out the total area of each rug. Write the price on the price tag.

1. $2.50
2. $19.57
3. $24
4. $4
5. $25
6. $15
7. $16
8. $15

45

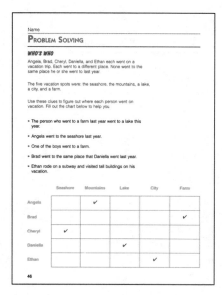

PROBLEM SOLVING

WHO'S WHO

Angela, Brad, Cheryl, Daniella, and Ethan each went on a vacation trip. Each went to a different place. None went to the same place he or she went to last year.

The five vacation spots were: the seashore, the mountains, a lake, a city, and a farm.

Use these clues to figure out where each person went on vacation. Fill out the chart below to help you.

- The person who went to a farm last year went to a lake this year.
- Angela went to the seashore last year.
- One of the boys went to a farm.
- Brad went to the same place that Daniella went last year.
- Ethan rode on a subway and visited tall buildings on his vacation.

	Seashore	Mountains	Lake	City	Farm
Angela		✓			
Brad					✓
Cheryl	✓				
Daniella			✓		
Ethan				✓	

46

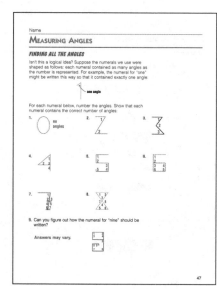

MEASURING ANGLES

FINDING ALL THE ANGLES

Isn't this a logical idea? Suppose the numerals we use were shaped as follows: each numeral contained as many angles as the number is represented. For example, the numeral for "one" might be written this way so that it contained exactly one angle.

one angle

For each numeral below, number the angles. Show that each numeral contains the correct number of angles:

1. no angles
2.
3.
4.
5.
6.
7.
8.

9. Can you figure out how the numeral for "nine" should be written?

Answers may vary.

47

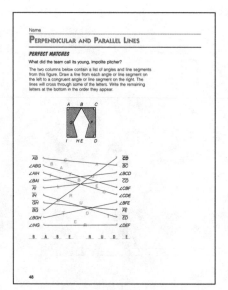

PERPENDICULAR AND PARALLEL LINES

PERFECT MATCHES

What did the team call its young, impolite pitcher?

The two columns below contain a list of angles and line segments from this figure. Draw a line from each angle or line segment on the left to a congruent angle or line segment on the right. The lines will cross through some of the letters. Write the remaining letters at the bottom in the order they appear.

$\overline{AB}$	$\overline{CD}$
$\angle ABG$	$\overline{BC}$
$\angle AIH$	$\overline{BCD}$
$\angle BAI$	$\overline{CD}$
$\overline{AI}$	$\angle CBF$
$\overline{IH}$	$\angle CDE$
$\overline{GH}$	$\angle BFE$
$\overline{BG}$	$\overline{FE}$
$\angle BGH$	$\overline{ED}$
$\angle IHG$	$\angle DEF$

B A B E   R U D E

48

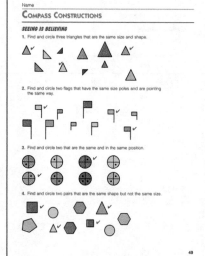

COMPASS CONSTRUCTIONS

SEEING IS BELIEVING

1. Find and circle three triangles that are the same size and shape.

2. Find and circle two flags that have the same size poles and are pointing the same way.

3. Find and circle two that are the same and in the same position.

4. Find and circle two pairs that are the same shape but not the same size.

49

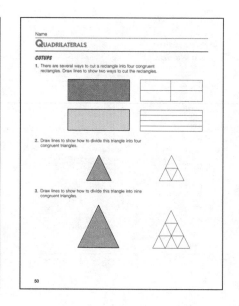

QUADRILATERALS

CUTUPS

1. There are several ways to cut a rectangle into four congruent rectangles. Draw lines to show two ways to cut the rectangles.

2. Draw lines to show how to divide this triangle into four congruent triangles.

3. Draw lines to show how to divide this triangle into nine congruent triangles.

50

72

ANSWER KEY

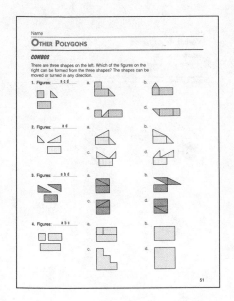

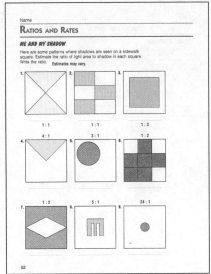

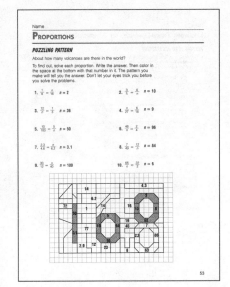

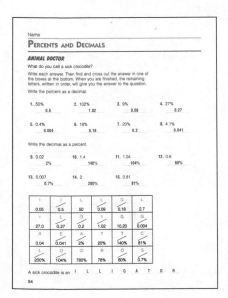

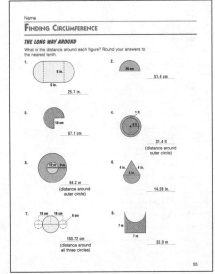

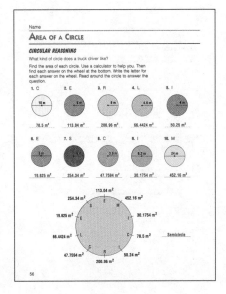

ANSWER KEY

Name

DRAWING THREE-DIMENSIONAL FIGURES

KEEPING IT IN PERSPECTIVE

A. When you draw space figures, give a feeling of depth. Draw in **perspective**. As you look at a real object, like railroad tracks, for example, parallel lines *seem* to get closer in the distance. When you draw, instead of drawing lines parallel, make them get closer in the distance, too.

Here are some rules:

- Use parallel lines for any surface facing you, like the front of this prism.
- Make lines of surfaces that are receding (going away) from you slant towards each other slightly, like the top of this prism.
- Use the same slant for lines that go in the same direction, like these lines.

Complete these figures. Use perspective.

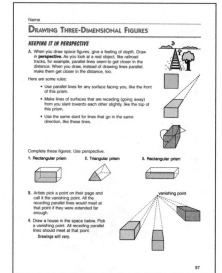

1. Rectangular prism 2. Triangular prism 3. Rectangular prism

B. Artists pick a point on their page and call it the vanishing point. All the receding parallel lines would meet at that point if they were extended far enough.

4. Draw a house in the space below. Pick a vanishing point. All receding parallel lines should meet at that point.

Drawings will vary.

vanishing point

57

VOLUME OF A TRIANGULAR PRISM

THINGS IN COMMON

In this diagram, the shapes in the left circle all have something in common. They are all shaded. The shapes in the right circle all have four or more straight sides. In the middle, where the circles overlap, are the shapes which fit into both groups—they are shaded with four or more straight sides.

← shapes outside the circles

For each diagram, decide where each shape should go. Then write the letter of each shape in the correct place. Write the letters of shapes that do not belong in any circle outside the circles.

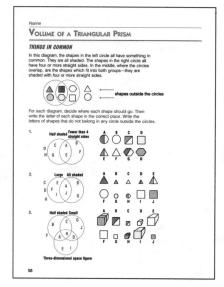

1. Half shaded Fewer than 4 straight sides

2. Large All shaded

3. Half shaded Small

Three-dimensional space figure

58

VOLUME OF A CYLINDER

CUTOUTS

Part of each of these three-dimensional figures has been cut out. Find the volume of the remainder.

Assume that when you see a shape cut out of one face of a figure, that cut goes through the entire figure. So, if you see a circle cut out of one side, the cutout figure is a cylinder.

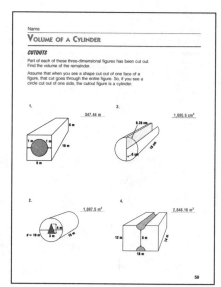

1. 347.44 m 3. 1,695.6 cm³

2. 1,087.5 m² 4. 2,848.16 m³

59

Name

PROBABILITY

MIX AND MATCH

A. There are ten white socks and ten black socks in a drawer. Tony reaches into the drawer without looking.

1. What is the probability that he will pick a white sock?

   1/2

2. What is the probability that he will pick a black sock?

   1/2

3. Tony picks a white sock. Now he needs a match. What is the probability that he will pick a white sock from the drawer on the next try?

   9/19

4. Tony picks a black sock. Now he has one white sock and one black sock. What is the probability that he will have a pair of matching socks on the next try?

   1 or 100%

5. Suppose the light is out so that Tony can't see the colors of the socks he picks. How many socks should he pick from the original 20 to be sure of getting at least one match?

   11

B. Assume that an equal number of people are born in each month.

6. If you try to guess the month someone is born in, what is the probability that you will guess the correct month?

   1/12

7. Suppose you are at a party with 35 people. You say that you can guarantee that you will find two people who were born in the same month if you can ask a certain number of people in what month he or she was born. What is the smallest number of people you can ask?

   13

60

LOGIC STATEMENTS

TRUE BLUE

The words *all*, *some*, or *no* (*none*) can be used to tell how two groups are related. Consider the following sentences:

All sparrows are birds.
Some birds are sparrows.
Some birds are not sparrows.
No birds are fish.

Notice that a sparrow is always a bird, but a bird is not always a sparrow (for example, a bird may be a robin). A bird is never a fish.

Write *true* or *false* for each statement.

1. All dogs are mammals. __T__

2. All mammals are dogs. __F__

3. Some mammals are dogs. __T__

4. No tables are mammals. __T__

5. All squares are quadrilaterals. __T__

6. Some quadrilaterals are not squares. __T__

7. Some squares are not polygons. __F__

8. All numbers greater than 40 are numbers greater than 30. __T__

9. Some numbers greater than 30 are numbers greater than 40. __T__

10. No even numbers are odd numbers. __T__

11. No odd numbers are numbers greater than 40. __F__

12. Some even numbers are not numbers that end in 0, 2, 4, 6, or 8. __F__

61

PROBLEM SOLVING

IT WORKS LIKE MAGIC

In a magic square, the sum of each row, column, and diagonal is the same. For example, here the sum is 150.

80	10	60
30	50	70
40	90	20

1. Look at the magic squares below. What do these squares and the one above have in common? (*Hint:* Think about simpler numbers.)

24	3	18
9	15	21
12	27	6

2⅔	⅓	2
1	1⅓	2⅓
1½	3	⅔

All are multiples of a square with these numbers:

8	1	6
3	5	7
4	9	2

2. Now use the same pattern to make two more magic squares.

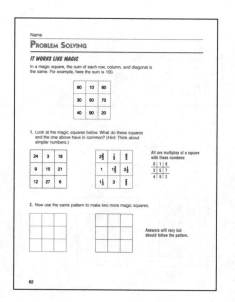

Answers will vary but should follow the pattern.

62

74

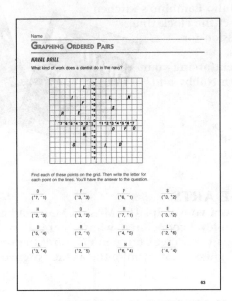

Name _____

GRAPHING ORDERED PAIRS

NAVAL DRILL

What kind of work does a dentist do in the navy?

Find each of these points on the grid. Then write the letter for each point on the lines. You'll have the answer to the question.

O	F	F	S
(⁻7, ⁻1)	(⁻3, ⁺3)	(⁺6, ⁻1)	(⁺3, ⁺2)

H	O	R	E
(⁻2, ⁻3)	(⁺3, ⁻2)	(⁻7, ⁺1)	(⁻3, ⁻2)

D	R	I	L
(⁺5, ⁻4)	(⁻2, ⁻1)	(⁻4, ⁺5)	(⁻2, ⁺6)

L	I	N	G
(⁺3, ⁺4)	(⁺2, ⁻5)	(⁺6, ⁺4)	(⁻4, ⁻4)

63

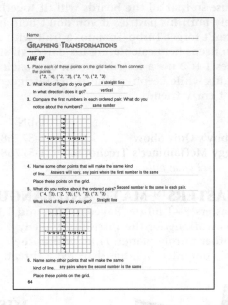

Name _____

GRAPHING TRANSFORMATIONS

LINE UP

1. Place each of these points on the grid below. Then connect the points.
   (⁺2, ⁻4), (⁺2, ⁻2), (⁺2, ⁺1), (⁺2, ⁺3)

2. What kind of figure do you get? __a straight line__
   In what direction does it go? __vertical__

3. Compare the first numbers in each ordered pair. What do you notice about the numbers? __same number__

4. Name some other points that will make the same kind of line. __Answers will vary, any pairs where the first number is the same__
   Place these points on the grid.

5. What do you notice about the ordered pairs? __Second number is the same in each pair.__
   (⁻4, ⁺3), (⁻2, ⁺3), (⁺1, ⁺3), (⁺3, ⁺3)
   What kind of figure do you get? __Straight line__

6. Name some other points that will make the same kind of line. __any pairs where the second number is the same__
   Place these points on the grid.

64

![McGraw-Hill logo] **McGraw-Hill Consumer Products**

The skills taught in school are now available at home!
These award-winning software titles meet school guidelines and are based on
The McGraw-Hill Companies classroom software titles.

MATH GRADES 1 & 2

These math programs are a great way to teach and reinforce skills used in everyday situations. Fun, friendly characters need help with their math skills. Everyone's friend, Nubby the stubby pencil, will help kids master the math in the Numbers Quiz show. Foggy McHammer, a carpenter, needs some help building his playhouse so that all the boards will fit together! Julio Bambino's kitchen antics will surely burn his pastries if you don't help him set the clock timer correctly! We can't forget Turbo Tomato, a fruit with a passion for adventure, who needs help calculating his daredevil stunts.

Math Grades 1 & 2 use a tested, proven approach to reinforcing your child's math skills while keeping him or her intrigued with Nubby and his collection of crazy friends.

TITLE	ISBN
Grade 1: Nubby's Quiz Show	1-57768-321-8
Grade 2: Foggy McHammer's Treehouse	1-57768-322-6

Available in jewel case only (no box included)

MISSION MASTERS™ MATH AND LANGUAGE ARTS

The Mission Masters™—Pauline, Rakeem, Mia, and T.J.—need your help. The Mission Masters™ are a team of young agents working for the Intelliforce Agency, a high-level cooperative whose goal is to maintain order on our rather unruly planet. From within the agency's top secret Command Control Center, the agency's central computer, M5, has detected a threat...and guess what—you're the agent assigned to the mission!

MISSION MASTERS™ MATH GRADES 3, 4, & 5

This series of exciting activities encourages young mathematicians to challenge themselves and their math skills to overcome the perils of villains and other planetary threats. Skills reinforced include: analyzing and solving real-world problems, estimation, measurements, geometry, whole numbers, fractions, graphs, and patterns.

TITLE	ISBN
Grade 3: Mission Masters™ Defeat Dirty D!	1-57768-323-5
Grade 4: Mission Masters™ Alien Encounter	1-57768-324-2
Grade 5: Mission Masters™ Meet Mudflat Moe	1-57768-325-0

Available in jewel case only (no box included)

MISSION MASTERS™ LANGUAGE ARTS GRADES 3, 4, & 5

This series invites children to apply their language skills to defeat unscrupulous characters and to overcome other earthly dangers. Skills reinforced include: language mechanics and usage, punctuation, spelling, vocabulary, reading comprehension, and creative writing.

TITLE	ISBN
Grade 3: Mission Masters™ Freezing Frenzy	1-57768-343-9
Grade 4: Mission Masters™ Network Nightmare	1-57768-344-7
Grade 5: Mission Masters™ Mummy Mysteries	1-57768-345-5

Available in jewel case only (no box included)

BASIC SKILLS BUILDER K to 2 – THE MAGIC APPLEHOUSE

At the Magic Applehouse, children discover that Abigail Appleseed runs a deliciously successful business selling apple pies, tarts, and other apple treats. Enthusiasm grows as children join in the fun of helping Abigail run her business. Along the way they'll develop computer and entrepreneurial skills to last a lifetime. They will run their own business – all while they're having bushels of fun!

TITLE	ISBN
Basic Skills Builder –The Magic Applehouse	1-57768-312-9

Available in jewel case only (no box included)

TEST PREP – SCORING HIGH

This grade-based testing software will help prepare your child for standardized achievement tests given by his or her school. Scoring High specifically targets the skills required for success on the Stanford Achievement Test (SAT) for grades three through eight. Lessons and test questions follow the same format and cover the same content areas as questions appearing on the actual SAT tests. The practice tests are modeled after the SAT test-taking experience with similar directions, number of questions per section, and bubble-sheet answer choices.

Scoring High is a child's first-class ticket to a winning score on standardized achievement tests!

TITLE	ISBN
Grades 3 to 5: Scoring High Test Prep	1-57768-316-1
Grades 6 to 8: Scoring High Test Prep	1-57768-317-X

Available in jewel case only (no box included)

SCIENCE

Mastering the principles of both physical and life science has never been so FUN for kids grades six and above as it is while they are exploring McGraw-Hill's edutainment software!

TITLE	ISBN
Grades 6 & up: Life Science	1-57768-336-6
Grades 8 & up: Physical Science	1-57768-308-0

Available in jewel case only (no box included)

REFERENCE

The National Museum of Women in the Arts has teamed with McGraw-Hill Consumer Products to bring you this superb collection available for your enjoyment on CD-ROM.

This special collection is a visual diary of 200 women artists from the Renaissance to the present, spanning 500 years of creativity.

You will discover the art of women who excelled in all the great art movements of history. Artists who pushed the boundaries of abstract, genre, landscape, narrative, portrait, and still-life styles; as well as artists forced to push the societal limits placed on women through the ages.

TITLE	ISBN
Women in the Arts	1-57768-010-3

Available in boxed version only

Most titles for Windows 3.1™, Windows '95™ & '98™, and Macintosh™.

Visit us on the Internet at:

www.MHkids.com

Or call 800-298-4119 for your local retailer.

McGraw-Hill Consumer Products

All our workbooks meet school curriculum guidelines and correspond to The McGraw-Hill Companies classroom textbooks.

SPECTRUM SERIES

DOLCH Sight Word Activities

The DOLCH Sight Word Activities Workbooks use the classic Dolch list of 220 basic vocabulary words that make up from 50% to 75% of all reading matter that children ordinarily encounter. Since these words are ordinarily recognized on sight, they are called *sight words*. Volume 1 includes 110 sight words. Volume 2 covers the remainder of the list. Over 160 pages.

TITLE	ISBN
Grades K-1 Vol. 1	1-57768-429-X
Grades K-1 Vol. 2	1-57768-439-7

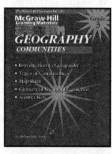

GEOGRAPHY

Full-color, three-part lessons strengthen geography knowledge and map reading skills. Focusing on five geographic themes including location, place, human/environmental interaction, movement, and regions. Over 150 pages. Glossary of geographical terms and answer key included.

TITLE	ISBN
Gr 3, Communities	1-57768-153-3
Gr 4, Regions	1-57768-154-1
Gr 5, USA	1-57768-155-X
Gr 6, World	1-57768-156-8

MATH

Features easy-to-follow instructions that give students a clear path to success. This series has comprehensive coverage of the basic skills, helping children to master math fundamentals. Over 150 pages. Answer key included.

TITLE	ISBN
Grade 1	1-57768-111-8
Grade 2	1-57768-112-6
Grade 3	1-57768-113-4
Grade 4	1-57768-114-2
Grade 5	1-57768-115-0
Grade 6	1-57768-116-9
Grade 7	1-57768-117-7
Grade 8	1-57768-118-5

PHONICS

Provides everything children need to build multiple skills in language. Focusing on phonics, structural analysis, and dictionary skills, this series also offers creative ideas for using phonics and word study skills in other language arts. Over 200 pages. Answer key included.

TITLE	ISBN
Grade K	1-57768-120-7
Grade 1	1-57768-121-5
Grade 2	1-57768-122-3
Grade 3	1-57768-123-1
Grade 4	1-57768-124-X
Grade 5	1-57768-125-8
Grade 6	1-57768-126-6

READING

This full-color series creates an enjoyable reading environment, even for below-average readers. Each book contains captivating content, colorful characters, and compelling illustrations, so children are eager to find out what happens next. Over 150 pages. Answer key included.

TITLE	ISBN
Grade K	1-57768-130-4
Grade 1	1-57768-131-2
Grade 2	1-57768-132-0
Grade 3	1-57768-133-9
Grade 4	1-57768-134-7
Grade 5	1-57768-135-5
Grade 6	1-57768-136-3

SPELLING

This full-color series links spelling to reading and writing and increases skills in words and meanings, consonant and vowel spellings, and proofreading practice. Over 200 pages. Speller dictionary and answer key included.

TITLE	ISBN
Grade 1	1-57768-161-4
Grade 2	1-57768-162-2
Grade 3	1-57768-163-0
Grade 4	1-57768-164-9
Grade 5	1-57768-165-7
Grade 6	1-57768-166-5

WRITING

Lessons focus on creative and expository writing using clearly stated objectives and pre-writing exercises. Eight essential reading skills are applied. Activities include main idea, sequence, comparison, detail, fact and opinion, cause and effect, and making a point. Over 130 pages. Answer key included.

TITLE	ISBN
Grade 1	1-57768-141-X
Grade 2	1-57768-142-8
Grade 3	1-57768-143-6
Grade 4	1-57768-144-4
Grade 5	1-57768-145-2
Grade 6	1-57768-146-0
Grade 7	1-57768-147-9
Grade 8	1-57768-148-7

TEST PREP
From the Nation's #1 Testing Company

Prepares children to do their best on current editions of the five major standardized tests. Activities reinforce test-taking skills through examples, tips, practice, and timed exercises. Subjects include reading, math, and language. Over 150 pages. Answer key included.

TITLE	ISBN
Grade 1	1-57768-101-0
Grade 2	1-57768-102-9
Grade 3	1-57768-103-7
Grade 4	1-57768-104-5
Grade 5	1-57768-105-3
Grade 6	1-57768-106-1
Grade 7	1-57768-107-X
Grade 8	1-57768-108-8

LANGUAGE ARTS

Encourages creativity and builds confidence by making writing fun! Seventy-two four-part lessons strengthen writing skills by focusing on parts of speech, word usage, sentence structure, punctuation, and proofreading. Each level includes a *Writer's Handbook* at the end of the book that offers writing tips. This series is based on the highly respected SRA/McGraw-Hill language arts series. More than 180 full-color pages. *Available March 2000.*

TITLE	ISBN
Grade 2	1-57768-472-9
Grade 3	1-57768-473-7
Grade 4	1-57768-474-5
Grade 5	1-57768-475-3
Grade 6	1-57768-476-1

READING

- Reading Comprehension
- Main Idea
- Study Skills
- Drawing Conclusions

From The Nation's #1 Educational Publisher K-12

Grade 6

Enrichment Reading

CONTENTS

NAME _____

FOLLOWING DIRECTIONS

Read each set of directions, then circle the letter choice that best answers the question about the directions.

DIRECTIONS: The only ingredients you will need are a cup of water and one and three quarters of a cup of granulated sugar. First boil the water. Then take it off the heat and stir in the sugar. For colored rock candy, add a drop or two of food coloring. Then let the solution cool. Next carefully heat a glass jar by running hot water over it, and pour in the sugar solution. Let the solution stand while you tie a string around a pencil that is longer than the mouth of the jar. Make sure that the length of the string is the same as the height of the jar. Then place the pencil across the top of the jar with the string hanging down into the solution. As the solution stands for several days, the sugar crystals will form around the string.

---

1. These directions show you how to—
   (A) make rock candy
   (B) make a sugar syrup
   (C) freeze sugar
   (D) purify sugar

2. Before stirring the sugar into the water,—
   (A) tie the string to the pencil
   (B) boil the water
   (C) heat a glass jar well
   (D) put the string into the water

3. After the sugar solution cools,—
   (A) pour it into a cool jar
   (B) pour it into a heated jar
   (C) stand a pencil in it
   (D) add food coloring

4. The sugar crystals will form—
   (A) around the pencil
   (B) in a few days
   (C) almost immediately
   (D) when you add more sugar

3

GETTING THE MAIN IDEA

Read the stories, then, on the opposite page, circle the letter choice for the sentence that tells the main idea of the story.

---

1.   Compared with the fourteen-thousand-foot peaks of the Rockies, Mt. Washington in New Hampshire may seem relatively small at 6,288 feet high. However, the top of Mt. Washington has unbelievably treacherous weather. In moments the weather can change from a sunny to a stormy day—often with fierce gales. No wonder the building on this mountaintop is chained to the ground!

---

2.   Many fighters for women's equality say it's about time the United States put a woman's portrait on some of its paper money. Few people know, however, that two women have already achieved that honor, a century ago. Martha Washington's face graced a one-dollar bill and Pocahontas' picture appeared on a twenty-dollar bank note.

---

3.   Trees use and give off a surprising amount of water. The water is taken in by the roots and released by the leaves. It has been estimated that eighty gallons of water a day may evaporate from the average tree. A white oak tree will give off 150 gallons of moisture in a single day during hot weather. A large oak tree will give off 28,000 gallons of water during one growing season!

---

4.   The North Pole is not the world's coldest region. Northeastern Siberia, over one thousand miles south of the North Pole, is the coldest place on earth. Temperatures as low as eighty degrees below zero Fahrenheit (-62.2 Celsius) have often been recorded. Oddly enough, you would seldom catch a cold in the world's coldest region. Most germs cannot live in such extreme cold!

---

5.   The mystery of how salmon can find their way back to their home rivers is solved. A salmon navigates by sun and stars when traveling in the ocean. When the salmon nears the general area of the river in which it was born, it uses its nose. The salmon can remember the smell of the home river that it left as a baby.

GETTING THE MAIN IDEA

1. The paragraph tells mainly—
    (A) why people climb to the top of Mt. Washington
    (B) why Mt. Washington is smaller than the Rockies
    (C) why the weather can change so fast at the top of Mt. Washington
    (D) why the top of Mt. Washington is treacherous

2. The paragraph tells mainly—
    (A) why women should be pictured on paper money
    (B) when women's portraits were printed on paper money
    (C) how people fight for equality
    (D) why women are no longer pictured on paper money

3. The paragraph tells mainly—
    (A) how much water trees give off
    (B) how trees give off water
    (C) what trees give off the least water
    (D) how trees take in water

4. The paragraph tells mainly—
    (A) how cold it gets
    (B) why people don't catch cold
    (C) what the coldest region is like
    (D) what the North Pole is like

5. The paragraph tells mainly—
    (A) what a mystery is
    (B) how far salmon travel
    (C) what salmon remember
    (D) how salmon find their way home

DRAWING CONCLUSIONS

Read the short stories, then, on the opposite page, circle the letter choice that describes something you can tell from the information in the story. Use clues in each story to draw a conclusion to find the correct answer.

1.　　English women once thought they looked best with wigs that rose two or even three feet above their heads. They certainly looked taller. Wool, cotton, and goats' hair were used to give the hairpieces the desired height. The finest high-piled wigs were often decorated with imitation fruit, model ships, horses, and figurines.

2.　　Though Americans take pride in the accomplishments of the pony express, few people know of an earlier and equally remarkable postal service. Eight hundred years before the pony express operated, messages traveled 150 miles a day—without the aid of a horse! Inca Indian runners were spaced about three miles apart over a stone road that stretched five thousand miles. These relay runners were the "express mail" carriers of their time.

3.　　When a large number of soldiers march across a small bridge, they are usually told to break step. If the bridge isn't particularly strong and the soldiers march in step, they can start a vibration that can cause the bridge to collapse. That is also the main reason why trains go slowly across bridges. A faster motion could set up vibrations and increase the danger of a bridge disaster.

4.　　The liver is the largest of the body's glands. It helps the body absorb food by producing a fluid that breaks down the food taken into the body. The liver keeps a close watch on the bloodstream, clearing the blood of many harmful products it can absorb. The liver also stores sugar for future use and makes sure that the heart does not become overloaded with blood.

5.　　By actually fishing for and catching other fish, the angler fish grows to be almost four feet long. It lies quietly in mud at the bottom of the water. Three wormlike "fingers" on the top of its head attract other fish. When the fish come close, the angler fish gets its meal. If fishing is slow, the angler fish may rise to the surface and swallow ducks, loons, or even geese.

DRAWING CONCLUSIONS

1. From the story you cannot tell—
   - (A) how wigs were decorated
   - (B) how high the wigs were
   - (C) what the wigs were made of
   - (D) the color of the wigs

2. The best nickname for these Indian messengers would be—
   - (A) Pony Express
   - (B) Inca Express
   - (C) Eight-hundred-year Mail
   - (D) Horseless Carriage

3. Trains go slowly across bridges—
   - (A) because bridges are long
   - (B) because trains are long
   - (C) for more than one reason
   - (D) because most bridges are weak

4. The liver performs—
   - (A) one function
   - (B) two functions
   - (C) four functions
   - (D) three functions

5. You can conclude that angler fish—
   - (A) prefer fish to other animals
   - (B) have worms growing out of their heads
   - (C) are often eaten by birds
   - (D) always remain at the bottom of the water

IDENTIFYING INFERENCES

Read the short stories. On the opposite page, read the sentences about each story. Decide whether each sentence is true (T), false (F), or an inference (I). A true sentence tells a fact from the story. A false sentence tells something that is not true. An inference says something that is *probably* true, based on facts in the story. More than one sentence about each story may be true, false, or an inference. Place an X in the correct box to mark your answer.

1. Mr. Gomes noticed a fresh, slick stain on the floor of his garage, right where the front of his car usually stops. "Oh, oh," he thought. "Something's leaking from my car." He bent down and sniffed the stain. "Doesn't smell like oil." He checked the water in the radiator and the brake fluid. "Both full. No leaks there. I don't have power steering or air conditioning, and my windshield-washer-fluid container has been empty for months. There are no other possibilities. It's a mystery."

2. "Who hid my hat?" asked Ralph angrily. "I know one of you did."
    "Why would anyone want to hide your hat?" inquired Tanya.
    Ralph scowled. "I know you all dislike me, and I don't care. Everyone's been against me from the moment I arrived here from my other school," said Ralph to his classmates. "Well, you won't have to put up with me anymore. I'm leaving!" Ralph grabbed his coat off the rack. When he did, his hat fell out from underneath. Ralph had hidden his hat from himself.

3. "We're out of eggs, Sis," Willis complained. "We can't make the supper."
    "I was afraid we might be," declared Sis. "In this cold weather, Mom usually stops at the Hope Diner on her way home from work for a cup of hot tea. The waiter knows her. Let's call the diner and leave a message for her." Sis dialed the diner.
    An hour later Mom came in with a bag of groceries, but no eggs.

4. "You said there was a river near here. Why don't we go swimming?" suggested Tina.
    "Oh, you wouldn't want to swim in that river!" said Karen.
    "Why not?" Tina asked. "I'm a strong swimmer. Even if the river's deep or the current's fast, it won't bother me."
    "It's not that the river is fast or deep," said Karen. "If you like swimming with tires, bottles and rusty cans, you can swim there."
    "Well," said Tina, "I don't particularly want to swim in a polluted river. Let's think of something better to do."

5. Kim was delighted to visit her cousin in Mexico, but she hadn't expected such hot weather. "I really can't stand this heat," she confided to her cousin.
    "Tomorrow will be better," her cousin assured her. "I've arranged for us to swim in our neighbor's outdoor pool."
    "Oh boy!" shouted Kim. "A plunge into cold, refreshing water. I can't wait!"
    "Er, uh," sighed her cousin, "don't get your hopes up too high."

8

IDENTIFYING INFERENCES

		T	F	I
1.	(A) Mr. Gomes considered six possibilities for the leak.	☒	☐	☐
	(B) Mr. Gomes will ask a mechanic to solve the mystery.	☐	☐	☒
	(C) The liquid stain smelled like oil.	☐	☒	☐
	(D) Mr. Gomes solved the mystery.	☐	☒	☐

		T	F	I
2.	(A) Tanya was sitting on Ralph's hat.	☐	☐	☐
	(B) Ralph had previously attended another school.	☐	☐	☐
	(C) Ralph expected people to pick on him.	☐	☐	☐
	(D) Ralph's hat was under his coat.	☐	☐	☐

		T	F	I
3.	(A) Mom had gone shopping instead of stopping at the diner for tea.	☐	☐	☐
	(B) Willis discovered that there were no eggs in the house.	☐	☐	☐
	(C) Mom had a dozen eggs in her bag of groceries.	☐	☐	☐
	(D) Sis decided to call the diner and leave a message.	☐	☐	☐

		T	F	I
4.	(A) The weather was warm enough for outdoor swimming.	☐	☐	☐
	(B) No other outdoor pools or bodies of water were located nearby.	☐	☐	☐
	(C) Tina was afraid to swim in a river with a fast current.	☐	☐	☐
	(D) Karen told Tina about the trash in the river.	☐	☐	☐

		T	F	I
5.	(A) The pool water could not be cooled in any way.	☐	☐	☐
	(B) The neighbors had an indoor pool.	☐	☐	☐
	(C) Kim had not expected Mexico to be so hot.	☐	☐	☐
	(D) Kim did not enjoy visiting her cousin.	☐	☐	☐

GETTING THE FACTS

Read the story, then, on the opposite page, circle the letter choice that best completes each sentence about the story.

Pioneer Woman of the Sky

Lightning ripped through the blackness over the mid-Atlantic Ocean. The small plane's engine sputtered. The slim young woman at the controls knew she was too far out to turn back. Carefully she coaxed the plane ahead through the storm.

When dawn came, the engine was failing seriously. Just ahead lay the Irish coast. As the engine gasped its last, the woman brought her plane down in a cow pasture. An astonished farmer raced over as the young woman climbed out of the airplane. "I'm from America," she said. "My name is Amelia Earhart." She had become the first woman ever to fly the Atlantic alone. She had even set a new speed record, thirteen hours and thirty minutes!

Many people had told Amelia Earhart not to make this flight. They didn't think a woman was strong enough to keep going through the long night. However, Earhart had strength and courage to spare. She had already made parachute jumps and had explored the ocean floor in a diver's suit. Now, overnight, she had become famous.

She then began to dream of circling the globe at its widest part. Money was raised, and Earhart bought a new plane. In her first attempt, however, her plane was damaged on takeoff and she had to delay the flight. By the time the plane was repaired, the season had changed.

The world anxiously followed her flight. She flew across central Africa, Arabia, and the Orient. Finally, only one difficult stop remained. She would have to find a tiny speck in the Pacific—Howland Island.

As the world waited, a message crackled from her radio. People could not believe it. The message said, "Circling . . . cannot see island . . . gas is running low." For two weeks, warships and planes searched the ocean for the daring young woman and her copilot, Fred Noonan. No trace was ever found.

Today many airplanes, both commercial and military, follow the path blazed in the sky by the fearless woman aviator—Amelia Earhart.

GETTING THE FACTS

1. The woman at the controls was flying—
   - (A) a kite
   - (B) a jumbo jet
   - (C) through a storm
   - (D) with two copilots

2. She brought the airplane down—
   - (A) on a beach
   - (B) in a cow pasture
   - (C) in a deserted village
   - (D) in Boston

3. Amelia Earhart was the first woman to—
   - (A) fly the Atlantic alone
   - (B) cross America
   - (C) fly solo
   - (D) fly to Miami

4. Amelia made her trip in a little over—
   - (A) thirteen hours
   - (B) twenty hours
   - (C) six hours
   - (D) fifty hours

5. Amelia had also explored—
   - (A) the Klondike region
   - (B) Africa
   - (C) the jungle
   - (D) the ocean floor

6. She planned to—
   - (A) reach the South Pole
   - (B) circle the globe
   - (C) reach China
   - (D) reach the Arctic

7. On takeoff her airplane—
   - (A) caught fire
   - (B) was damaged
   - (C) crashed
   - (D) rose sharply

8. Amelia Earhart intended to land—
   - (A) in Japan
   - (B) on Howland Island
   - (C) in the Marshalls
   - (D) in Panama

9. A message from Amelia said that—
   - (A) her copilot was ill
   - (B) her time was up
   - (C) all was well
   - (D) the gas was low

10. Amelia and her plane—
    - (A) disappeared
    - (B) circled the globe
    - (C) reached Honolulu
    - (D) landed safely

DETECTING THE SEQUENCE

Read the story. As you read it, look for clues that let you know the order in which things happened. Then, on the opposite page, circle the letter choice that best answers the question about the sequence of events.

Elizabeth Blackwell, M.D.

In the early autumn of 1847, the professors of Geneva Medical College in New York held a meeting. Among the matters they discussed was a letter from Dr. William Elder of Philadelphia recommending that they admit Elizabeth Blackwell to the school. The professors were shocked. No American woman had ever been to an American medical school before. The idea of a woman doctor was ridiculous! They chose to pass the decision along to the students. Surely the young men would vote against Miss Blackwell. To the professors' surprise, they were wrong.

Elizabeth Blackwell received a letter from Geneva Medical College in late October telling her she could enter the school. Many months before, Blackwell had applied to thirty medical schools, but Geneva was the only one to admit her. On November 6, 1847, she attended her first lecture at Geneva Medical College. Two years later, she graduated at the top of her class.

Now Dr. Blackwell wanted to become a surgeon, and she traveled to Paris to continue her studies. None of the teaching hospitals there would accept a woman doctor, however, so she entered Paris' largest women's hospital as a nursing student instead. Four months after she began working there, Dr. Blackwell caught an eye infection from a patient. She lost her sight in one eye, thus ruining her chances to become a surgeon.

In 1851, Dr. Blackwell settled in New York City. She set up a doctor's office, but her landlord refused to let her hang up a sign. No patients came for months. Meanwhile, she presented a series of lectures on "the physical education of girls." Stacy Collins, one of the women in the audience, was so impressed with Dr. Blackwell that she became the doctor's first patient.

By 1854, Dr. Blackwell was able to make a living as a doctor. Three years later, she opened a hospital, the New York Infirmary for Women and Children. During its first year, the hospital treated three hundred patients. The next year, however, it treated three thousand. Still, Dr. Blackwell had even higher hopes. She urged New York to start a women's medical college. Finally, in 1866, the New York Women's Medical College held its first class. Among the professors teaching there was Elizabeth Blackwell, M.D.

DETECTING THE SEQUENCE

1. **Which of these events happened first?**

    (A) Elizabeth Blackwell traveled to Paris to study.

    (B) Elizabeth Blackwell applied to thirty medical schools.

    (C) Elizabeth Blackwell attended her first lecture at Geneva Medical College.

    (D) Students at Geneva voted whether to admit Elizabeth Blackwell.

2. **Which of these events happened last?**

    (A) Elizabeth Blackwell settled in New York City.

    (B) Stacy Collins became Dr. Blackwell's first patient.

    (C) Dr. Blackwell taught at the New York Women's Medical College.

    (D) The New York Infirmary for Women and Children treated 300 patients.

3. **What happened soon after Dr. Blackwell began working at Paris' largest women's hospital?**

    (A) The hospital treated three thousand patients.

    (B) She caught an eye infection from a patient.

    (C) Geneva Medical College admitted her.

    (D) She presented a series of lectures.

4. **Which occurred after Dr. Blackwell presented lectures on "the physical education of girls"?**

    (A) Stacy Collins became Dr. Blackwell's first patient.

    (B) Geneva Medical College admitted Elizabeth Blackwell.

    (C) Dr. Blackwell set up a doctor's office in New York.

    (D) Dr. Blackwell traveled to Paris to continue her studies.

5. **When did Dr. Blackwell open the New York Infirmary for Women and Children?**

    (A) while she attended Geneva Medical College

    (B) after she taught at the New York Women's Medical College

    (C) before she studied nursing in Paris

    (D) after she set up a doctor's office in New York

FOLLOWING DIRECTIONS

Read each set of directions, then circle the letter choice that best answers the question about the directions.

DIRECTIONS: The TV weather report announces a tornado warning! It tells you to take shelter. Turn off all electrical devices. If you have a battery-powered radio, keep it with you. If you live in a mobile home, go to a community storm shelter. In a house or apartment, do not open windows. Open windows do not prevent severe wind damage. Go to a basement and get under a table or workbench. If you have no basement, go to an inner area far from windows, such as a hallway, inner bedroom, or closet. Crouch under a mattress or other thick bedding. Stay sheltered until the storm is over.

1. This paragraph was written to tell you how to—
   (A) take shelter during a storm   (B) turn off the electricity
   (C) draw a plan of your home   (D) choose a battery radio

2. Opening windows is not helpful because—
   (A) you will get cold   (B) rain will soak the floor
   (C) it wastes time   (D) wind damage still occurs

3. Getting under a workbench or table protects you from—
   (A) rain   (B) lightning
   (C) cold   (D) flying or falling material

4. Halls, inner bedrooms, or closets are safest because—
   (A) they are stronger   (B) they are away from the wind
   (C) they have a workbench   (D) they have been painted recently

USING THE CONTEXT

Read each set of sentences. In each set of sentences, there are two blanks. Circle the letter choice for the correct word that goes in each blank.

It's now possible to fly fairly close to a hospital in the thick jungle of Africa. The hospital, near Lambarene, was (1) _____ by Dr. Schweitzer in 1913. Each of the (2) _____ who visit Schweitzer Hospital annually is asked to donate a pint of blood.

1. **(A) computed**   **(B) alphabetized**   **(C) established**   **(D) barbecued**
2. **(A) skeletons**   **(B) pigeons**   **(C) submarines**   **(D) tourists**

People sometimes capture birds and place metal bands around their legs. Then the birds are released. When the banded birds are caught again, the metal tags tell where the birds have come from. Bird banding helps scientists (3) _____ more (4) _____ about the travel habits of birds.

3. **(A) send**   **(B) overlook**   **(C) gain**   **(D) grow**
4. **(A) messengers**   **(B) trips**   **(C) caution**   **(D) information**

Instead of producing a timid squeal, the grasshopper mouse makes a sound like a wolf. Its (5) _____ can be heard 100 yards away. This fearless mouse not only eats grasshoppers but also attacks creatures three times its size. Yet it (6) _____ other mice in appearance.

5. **(A) purr**   **(B) neigh**   **(C) baa**   **(D) howl**
6. **(A) outlaws**   **(B) weaves**   **(C) smells**   **(D) resembles**

Southeast of Japan is a stretch of water that the Japanese know as the Devil's Sea. Between 1950 and 1954 nine large freighters (7) _____ in this area without a (8) _____ . A vessel sent out to search the area vanished also, complete with crew and scientists!

7. **(A) reappeared**   **(B) vanished**   **(C) collided**   **(D) assembled**
8. **(A) warning**   **(B) sound**   **(C) trace**   **(D) signal**

Blood circulates through the body in blood vessels. There are more of these than you might (9) _____ . If they were (10) _____ in a row, the vessels would stretch for 100,000 miles, enough to circle the earth four times.

9. **(A) imagine**   **(B) doubt**   **(C) sing**   **(D) wonder**
10. **(A) piled**   **(B) laid**   **(C) buried**   **(D) hidden**

GETTING THE MAIN IDEA

Read the stories, then, on the opposite page, circle the letter choice for the sentence that tells the main idea of the story.

1.   The practice of wearing rings is a very ancient one. Over time, people in many lands have decorated their bodies by wearing rings on their fingers, ears, lips, necks, noses, ankles, and wrists. Some even wore rings on their toes. In some cultures, a married woman wore a ring on the big toe of her left foot; a man might put rings on his second and third toes as well.

2.   The frankfurter, named for the city of Frankfurt in Germany, is easily the most popular sausage in the world. Frankfurters, popularly known as "hot dogs," are sold almost everywhere in the United States. They are consumed in great numbers at sporting events and amusement places. People from foreign countries often think hot dogs are one of the characteristics of American life.

3.   Many ancient coins are not as valuable as people tend to think they are. In the early days the threat of a foreign invasion was common. People buried the family wealth, hoping to uncover it later when the threat was past. In many cases these people were killed or taken away as prisoners. Their coins are continually being uncovered by chance today and can be purchased for a modest price.

4.   The Trans-Canadian Highway is the first ocean-to-ocean highway in Canada and the longest paved road in the world. After twelve years of work, the 4,859-mile highway was completed in September of 1962. The Trans-Canadian Highway makes it possible, for the first time, for a person to drive from coast to coast and remain within Canada for the entire trip.

5.   The experts are not always right. They advised the big mining companies to pass up the Cripple Creek region. They claimed that there was no gold there. It was left up to local prospectors to uncover the incredible wealth of Cripple Creek. More than $400 million worth of ore was found in this area that experts ignored.

GETTING THE MAIN IDEA

1. The paragraph tells mainly—

    (A) why some people wore rings on their toes

    (B) what kinds of rings were the most popular

    (C) when the practice of wearing rings first began

    (D) how people in many lands have worn rings

2. The paragraph tells mainly—

    (A) why hot dogs are popular

    (B) how popular hot dogs are

    (C) what foreign people think of hot dogs

    (D) how hot dogs and frankfurters differ

3. The paragraph tells mainly—

    (A) what happened during invasions

    (B) why there are so few ancient coins today

    (C) why many ancient coins are inexpensive

    (D) why people were taken prisoners

4. The paragraph tells mainly—

    (A) what the Trans-Canadian Highway is like

    (B) how the Trans-Canadian Highway helps

    (C) why the Trans-Canadian Highway was built

    (D) where the longest road is

5. The paragraph tells mainly—

    (A) what experts thought about Cripple Creek

    (B) when the Cripple Creek gold was found

    (C) how much the ore was worth

    (D) how big mining companies operated

PROGRESS CHECK

Exploring Language

What makes a joke funny? To understand the humor of a joke, you need to draw conclusions about it. Read each of the following jokes. Answer the questions about the jokes.

1. Jan asked her teacher, "Would you scold someone for something she didn't do?" "Of course not," her teacher answered. "Why do you ask?" "Because I didn't do my math homework," Jan answered.

   What did the teacher mean when she said that she wouldn't scold someone for something she didn't do?

   _____

   _____

   _____

2. A traveler asked the ticket agent at a railroad station for a round trip ticket. "Where to?" the ticket agent asked. "Back to here," the traveler said.

   What did the ticket agent want to know?

   _____

   _____

   _____

3. Willy asked Billy, "Were you born in New York?" "Yes," Billy answered. "What part?" asked Willy. "All of me," said Billy.

   What did Willy want to know?

   _____

   _____

   _____

NAME _____

PROGRESS CHECK

Exercising Your Skill

An **analogy** is a way of comparing things. When we make an analogy, we are saying that things that are otherwise unlike *are* similar in some way. We are pointing out a relationship between two sets of things. For example:

Pitcher is to **baseball** as **quarterback** is to **football**.

In other words, a pitcher is one of the players in a baseball game, just as a quarterback is one of the players in a football game.

Analogies may show many different kinds of relationships. They may relate words with similar meanings (synonyms), words with opposite meanings (antonyms), parts to the whole, users to things used, or actions to objects.

Read each item below and draw a conclusion about the relationship between the sets of things. Ask yourself whether there is a relationship between the two sets of things. For each analogy, write *sense* or *no sense* to tell whether you think the analogy makes sense.

1. The **moon** is to the **earth** as the **earth** is to the **sun**.
   sense

2. **Puzzle** is to **solution** as **lock** is to **key**.

3. **Needles** are to **pine tree** as **leaves** are to **autumn**.

4. **Reality** is to **fantasy** as **pleasure** is to **enjoyment**.

5. **Gray** is to **black** as **pink** is to **red**.

6. **Ship** is to **port** as **car** is to **garage**.

7. **Row** is to **boat** as **pedal** is to **bicycle**.

8. **Fox** is to **den** as **grizzly** is to **bear**.

9. **Pod** is to **pea** as **shell** is to **walnut**.

10. **Scissors** are to **sharp** as **stapler** is to **staple**.

IDENTIFYING INFERENCES

Read the short stories. On the opposite page, read the sentences about each story. Decide whether each sentence is true (T), false (F), or an inference (I). A true sentence tells a fact from the story. A false sentence tells something that is not true. An inference says something that is *probably* true, based on facts in the story. More than one sentence about each story may be true, false, or an inference. Place an X in the correct box to mark your answer.

1.   Lois waited for her turn to read her poem in front of the class. "This is a pretty good poem," she thought to herself. "It's just that. . . ." Then her name was called, she stood up, and her knees began to shake. When she turned around and looked at the rest of the class, however, she saw friendly faces. "Maybe this won't be so bad after all," Lois thought with relief.

2.   Tommy was happily skipping homeward, whacking trees and lightpoles with a thin stick as he went—just for fun. Suddenly, as he struck a pole, all the lights in town went out.

       Tommy groped his way home. His parents were listening to a battery-powered radio in the dark. He slinked past them and hid under his bed. "So the power failure is statewide," said Tommy's mother to his father. "The reporter said that it was definitely caused by a faulty generator miles upstate."

3.   The young man lay at the bottom of the cliff in a crumpled heap. The two girls who approached him thought he was dead, until. . . .

       "Please get help," he moaned in pain. "Call an ambulance." Dawn stayed with the man, while Grace ran to a nearby telephone.

       "What can I do to make you more comfortable?" asked Dawn.

       "Could you get these loops of rope off my leg?" he requested.

       Soon the ambulance arrived. The paramedics said the man had some broken ribs but that he would be all right.

4.   "Look at our new puppy—isn't he cute? We've named him Snowball," Craig said. "He needs to have puppy shots, though, and we don't know which doctor to take him to. Can you recommend a good vet?"

       "Of course!" his neighbor answered. "We always go to Dr. Sylvia Miller. She was just terrific when Patches was so sick last summer. She identified the problem right away, and Patches was healthy and purring again within just a few days."

5.   "The sun beamed down on the sweltering city streets. Carl and Evan moped along, sweating. "We've got to beat this heat," groaned Carl.

       "Let's take the subway to the beach," suggested Evan.

       "Neither one of us has enough money for the bus," said Carl. "We can't afford an air-conditioned movie, either."

       "I know," cried Evan. "Let's go to Benny's."

       "Great idea!" responded Carl, and they ran off.

IDENTIFYING INFERENCES

			T	F	I
1.	(A)	Lois went to the back of the room.		X	
	(B)	Lois was afraid of speaking in front of the class.			X
	(C)	As soon as Lois stood up, she felt calm.		X	
	(D)	The faces of her classmates were friendly.	X		

			T	F	I
2.	(A)	Tommy thought he had caused the power failure.			
	(B)	When Tommy arrived home, his parents were watching TV.			
	(C)	The cause of the power failure was far from Tommy's home.			
	(D)	The power failed because Tommy struck the pole.			

			T	F	I
3.	(A)	The girls found the young man at the bottom of the cliff.			
	(B)	The man asked the girls to call an ambulance.			
	(C)	The man had been mountain climbing.			
	(D)	At first the two girls thought the man was dead.			

			T	F	I
4.	(A)	Craig asked his neighbor to recommend a good vet.			
	(B)	Patches is the neighbor's pet cat.			
	(C)	The name of Craig's new puppy is Snowball.			
	(D)	Patches died last summer.			

			T	F	I
5.	(A)	Carl suggested going to the beach.			
	(B)	Benny's is a cool place.			
	(C)	The boys could not afford the subway or the movies.			
	(D)	Benny's is a place that costs little or no money.			

PROGRESS CHECK

Exploring Language

Choose one of these activities.

1. Here are several sentences about hurricanes. Look for the main idea sentence and its supporting sentences. Then rearrange the supporting sentences into a clear paragraph. Do not include the two sentences that do not support the main idea sentence. Finally, give the paragraph a title.

   - The eye of a hurricane is usually about 14 miles across.
   - Winds stretch out from the eye several hundred miles in all directions.
   - The shape of a hurricane is unique.
   - The word "hurricane" comes from a West Indian word, *huracan,* which means "evil spirit."
   - It is the only storm that has a calm center, or "eye."
   - Winds and rains around the eye are the strongest.
   - The hurricane season in the Northern Hemisphere lasts from June through November.
   - However, an eye twice the normal size is not unusual.
   - Air around the eye swirls upward like smoke in a chimney.

   _____

   _____

   _____

   _____

   _____

   _____

   _____

   _____

   _____

   _____

   Write your title for the paragraph. _____

   _____

2. Write four or five sentences on another piece of paper in support of the following main idea.

   The real damage from a hurricane occurs when the storm strikes an area where a lot of people live.

USING THE CONTEXT

Read each set of sentences. In each set of sentences, there are two blanks. Circle the letter choice for the correct word that goes in each blank.

When people apply perfume or after-shave lotion to their faces or behind their ears, only those friends and associates about a foot and a half taller than the users can (1) _____ the aroma well. Since odors rise, people should put pleasing scents on their (2) _____ or knees.

1. (A) honor   (B) detect   (C) unwrap   (D) dissolve
2. (A) foreheads   (B) hair   (C) ankles   (D) eyebrows

When the telephone first came into use, people considered it impolite to phone someone at home without being (3) _____ to do so. The first phone book was printed in 1870. It contained only 271 (4) _____ , none of which were personal. Only companies were listed.

3. (A) petitioned   (B) licensed   (C) qualified   (D) invited
4. (A) subjects   (B) listings   (C) categories   (D) classifications

Jules Verne, one of the first writers of science fiction, foresaw television a hundred years ago. He called it "phonotelephoto." He also foresaw the skyscrapers of today. Most remarkably, he (5) _____ the first trip to the (6) _____ from a launching spot near the one actually used!

5. (A) made   (B) predicted   (C) arranged   (D) recorded
6. (A) moon   (B) sun   (C) universe   (D) crater

(7) _____ in ancient Rome were highly (8) _____ . If the script called for a fire, the stage would be put to the torch. If an attack by a wild animal was indicated, an actor would engage in a fight to the death with a real live bear!

7. (A) Games   (B) Plays   (C) Contests   (D) Exhibits
8. (A) appealing   (B) artistic   (C) symbolic   (D) realistic

Would you be surprised if you saw a baby larger than its parents? This happens with birds. The parents stuff the baby with food. Within a few weeks the baby is often larger than either parent. When it flies off to (9) _____ for its own food, it (10) _____ weight.

9. (A) purchase   (B) gather   (C) raise   (D) search
10. (A) obtains   (B) remains   (C) loses   (D) gains

GETTING THE FACTS

Read the story, then, on the opposite page, circle the letter choice that best completes each sentence about the story.

Ghost Ship of World War II

"I don't believe it," said the sailor on board the United States Navy destroyer. It was during World War II, and the sailor was looking at an enemy ship. "That destroyer flies the Japanese flag," the sailor shouted, "but it looks like an American ship!" Then the guns of the strange warship opened fire, and once again the air over the Pacific Ocean rocked to the sounds of battle.

It was not the first time this dangerous warship had fired at the American navy. But no American sailor could ever figure out its name. It was not on any chart. It did not match any pictures of Japanese destroyers in navy files. Yet it looked like many other American ships. Soon American sailors were calling this mysterious craft the Ghost Ship of World War II.

The story of the Ghost Ship is a very strange one. On February 26, 1942, the American destroyer *Stewart* was damaged by the Japanese. It was ordered back to port for repairs. But Japanese airplanes attacked it again and scored a direct hit. American officers then ordered a retreat. The crew abandoned ship, and the *Stewart* was left behind.

Three weeks later the *Stewart* was taken off the list of U.S. Navy ships. But no one knew that the Japanese had captured the American warship and rebuilt it. Soon it was fighting side by side with Japanese destroyers. Time and time again, the Ghost Ship saw action against the American navy. Throughout the entire war, no American was able to solve the mystery.

But the end of the tale is even stranger. After the Americans won the war, they found an old rusty destroyer in a Japanese port. It had been abandoned by the Japanese. The Americans checked their records and lists of ships. They were surprised to find that the Japanese destroyer was really the old USS *Stewart*. The mystery of the Ghost Ship of World War II was finally solved.

GETTING THE FACTS

1. The strange enemy warship flew the flag of—
   - (A) Germany
   - (B) Italy
   - (C) Japan
   - (D) the United States

2. Both ships were traveling in the—
   - (A) Atlantic Ocean
   - (B) Indian Ocean
   - (C) Black Sea
   - (D) Pacific Ocean

3. American sailors named this craft the Ghost Ship of—
   - (A) World War III
   - (B) World War II
   - (C) Japan
   - (D) World War I

4. The name of the destroyer that was damaged by the Japanese was the—
   - (A) *Stewart*
   - (B) *Seaworth*
   - (C) *Saunders*
   - (D) *Stephen*

5. The destroyer was left behind by the—
   - (A) Japanese
   - (B) army
   - (C) marines
   - (D) navy

6. Unknown to the navy, the ship was captured by the—
   - (A) Army
   - (B) Japanese
   - (C) Russians
   - (D) Germans

7. After the war, the destroyer was—
   - (A) lost
   - (B) painted
   - (C) found
   - (D) sold

8. This time the Ghost Ship was discarded by the—
   - (A) Germans
   - (B) Chinese
   - (C) United States
   - (D) Japanese

9. Surprisingly, the Ghost Ship was really the—
   - (A) USS *Stewart*
   - (B) UAR *Stewart*
   - (C) USS *Stillman*
   - (D) SSU *Stewart*

10. The Ghost Ship mystery was—
    - (A) taped
    - (B) unknown
    - (C) solved
    - (D) recorded

PROGRESS CHECK

Exercising Your Skill

There are different kinds of directions. Some directions are the kind you see in workbooks and on tests. Some directions tell you how to do or make something. Others tell you how to carry out an experiment.

Read these sets of directions. Think about what the directions tell you to do. Match each set of directions with a title from the box. In the space provided, write the title that fits the directions.

```
Experiment Directions      Game Directions
How-To Directions          Workbook Directions
```

1. Read about ducks. Decide how the kinds of ducks are the same or different. Then underline the answer to each question.

    Title ___Workbook Directions_____

2. You can make bongo drums with two coffee cans—one large and one small—their lids, and some masking tape. Snap the lids onto the cans. Turn the cans upside down and stand them on a table. Have someone hold the cans while you wind tape around them to hold them together. Turn the cans right side up, and drum away with your hands.

    Title _____

3. Which reflects the sun's rays better, black or white? Put two thermometers in the sun. Cover one with a white cloth and one with a black cloth. After half an hour, take off the cloth and check the temperature. Which thermometer shows a lower temperature?

    Title _____

4. You will need seven or eight people and several different objects. All the players sit in a circle and sing a song together. Pass the objects around. When the song is over, everyone who is caught with an object has to make up a skit about it. When the skits are finished, start again. Skits can't be repeated. If someone can't think of a new skit, he or she is out!

    Title _____

USING THE CONTEXT

Read each set of sentences. In each set of sentences, there are two blanks. Circle the letter choice for the correct word that goes in each blank.

People act the way they do largely because of the way they eat. What they eat can govern their moods and (1) _____ . The old rule about choosing from all the major food groups still holds. The more people vary their diets, the more chance they have of getting the (2) _____ their brains need.

1. **(A) emotions**   **(B) ancestors**   **(C) reservations**   **(D) witnesses**
2. **(A) safety**   **(B) nourishment**   **(C) homework**   **(D) welcome**

In early history only the wealthy could afford handkerchiefs. They were made of an expensive material. When not in use they were placed where no one today would (3) _____ of (4) _____ them. They were hung from the belt!

3. **(A) try**   **(B) fear**   **(C) count**   **(D) think**
4. **(A) using**   **(B) keeping**   **(C) making**   **(D) saving**

In olden times the host kept heaping food on the plate, thinking the guest was too timid to ask for more. The guest had to turn the (5) _____ upside down to show that no more food was (6) _____ .

5. **(A) food**   **(B) host**   **(C) plate**   **(D) town**
6. **(A) there**   **(B) devoured**   **(C) eaten**   **(D) desired**

Shadows provide a popular form of entertainment. With practice you can cast a variety of amusing shadow figures on a wall. Keep your hands, of course, between the (7) _____ and the (8) _____ upon which you wish to throw the shadow.

7. **(A) shadow**   **(B) pocket**   **(C) people**   **(D) light**
8. **(A) surface**   **(B) people**   **(C) spell**   **(D) glow**

A substitute is being sought for asbestos, a remarkable, yet dangerous, mineral. It is excellent for fireproofing, as well as for insulating against cold, heat, noise, and electricity. However, when (9) _____ , it becomes deadly and causes cancer and (10) _____ respiratory diseases.

9. **(A) threatened**   **(B) inhaled**   **(C) recorded**   **(D) translated**
10. **(A) simple**   **(B) minor**   **(C) fatal**   **(D) unserious**

GETTING THE MAIN IDEA

Read the stories, then, on the opposite page, circle the letter choice for the sentence that tells the main idea of the story.

1. Japanese fishers long ago figured out how nature could help them catch fish. The fishers have trained big birds, called cormorants, to do most of their work. Fishing from boats at night, the Japanese hang fires in baskets over the sides of their boats. Fish are attracted by the fire. The cormorants, on leashes, grab the fish, and the fishers grab the fish from the birds.

2. The Johnstown flood was the worst in United States history. On the afternoon of May 31, 1889, heavy rains caused a dam to break fifteen miles above Johnstown, Pennsylvania. A wall of water about thirty feet high and weighing millions of tons raced down the valley, sweeping everything with it—houses, trees, locomotives, animals, telegraph poles, and over two thousand people!

3. In August of 1873 the first hydrogen-filled balloon was launched in Paris. It landed near a little village fifteen miles away. The peasants were terrified. They thought it was a monster from another world. One fired a shot into it, allowing the hydrogen to escape. Others tore the balloon to shreds with their pitchforks.

4. The Carlsbad Caverns of New Mexico contain the largest known single open space below the surface of the earth. This giant room is 4,270 feet long, 656 feet wide, and 328 feet high. A twenty-eight-story skyscraper could fit inside. To this day, parts of this cavern remain unexplored, even though many years have passed since it was first entered.

5. Many people believe that sleigh bells were merely ornamental. This is not so. Bells were once a necessary part of winter traffic. In the days when there were no sidewalks, people walked on the roads. Sleighs drawn through the snow were fast and silent. Moreover, sound was partly muffled by earmuffs. Sleighs not equipped with bells were a genuine danger to those walking in traffic.

GETTING THE MAIN IDEA

1. The paragraph tells mainly—
    (A) what kind of fish the Japanese catch
    (B) where the Japanese catch fish
    (C) how the Japanese catch fish
    (D) why the Japanese catch fish

2. The paragraph tells mainly—
    (A) what the cause of the Johnstown flood was
    (B) how fast the Johnstown flood destroyed the city
    (C) how destructive the Johnstown flood was
    (D) what people thought about the flood

3. The paragraph tells mainly—
    (A) what the first hydrogen-filled-balloon flight proved
    (B) what hydrogen is
    (C) what happened to the first hydrogen-filled balloon
    (D) why the first balloon was filled with hydrogen

4. The paragraph tells mainly—
    (A) why people explore the Carlsbad Caverns
    (B) who discovered the largest cave
    (C) what the height of the room is
    (D) how large one room in the Carlsbad Caverns is

5. The paragraph tells mainly—
    (A) why people once walked on the road
    (B) how fast sleighs were
    (C) why sleighs had bells
    (D) why there were accidents

DRAWING CONCLUSIONS

Read the short stories, then, on the opposite page, circle the letter choice that describes something you can tell from the information in the story. Use clues in each story to draw a conclusion to find the correct answer.

1.   If you were trying to fall asleep, would a dark, quiet room be the best place to go? French scientists have found that a boring situation brings on sleep better than darkness and silence. In this experiment, people who experienced the tiresome repeating of a sound or light fell asleep more easily than people in quiet darkness. Next time you can't get to sleep, listen to the faucet drip or watch the corner traffic light.

2.   Almost no plants can survive in the bone-dry soil of Africa's Sahara desert. Yet, cave paintings created six thousand years ago in southern Algeria show farmers grazing cattle on rich grasslands. Changes in climate and the failure of people to be careful of soil and water supplies turned the pastureland to desert. The Sahara continues to spread southward each year.

3.   For the most part, soldiers who fought in the Civil War had no means of identification. Before some battles, soldiers made their own identification tags. Before especially danger-ous attacks, some Union soldiers cut slips of paper and pinned them to the backs of their coats, so that their dead bodies could be identified when the battle was over.

4.   Some of the tricks played by tornadoes seem unbelievable. One tornado whisked all the feathers from a chicken, leaving the animal embarrassed but otherwise unharmed. Another snatched the covers off a surprised sleeper. Still other tornadoes have carried mirrors for miles, leaving them undamaged, without as much as a single crack!

5.   Few animals can leap like the kangaroo. A full-grown kangaroo can make jumps of twenty feet when it is in flight. It can also clear fences eight feet high. Even when an enemy catches up with it, the kangaroo is a difficult opponent. The kangaroo is also an excellent boxer, using its front paws. Its powerful tail can cause great damage, too.

DRAWING CONCLUSIONS

1. People trying to stay awake should—
   - (A) watch a slowly blinking light
   - (B) listen to a repeated sound
   - (C) read an exciting book
   - (D) read a dull book

2. The writer does not suggest that—
   - (A) cave paintings give information about the past
   - (B) more rain used to fall in the region of the Sahara
   - (C) southern Algeria is in the Sahara desert
   - (D) people can change the Sahara back to farmland

3. You can tell that—
   - (A) all soldiers always expected to die
   - (B) many soldiers thought they might be killed
   - (C) no soldiers thought that they would be killed
   - (D) soldiers didn't want anyone to know who they were

4. You can tell that tornadoes—
   - (A) don't occur very often
   - (B) are more harmful than playful
   - (C) never do any harm
   - (D) play freakish tricks

5. The number of defenses listed for a kangaroo is—
   - (A) two
   - (B) three
   - (C) four
   - (D) five

IDENTIFYING INFERENCES

Read the short stories. On the opposite page, read the sentences about each story. Decide whether each sentence is true (T), false (F), or an inference (I). A true sentence tells a fact from the story. A false sentence tells something that is not true. An inference says something that is *probably* true, based on facts in the story. More than one sentence about each story may be true, false, or an inference. Place an X in the correct box to mark your answer.

1.   Mel's very first customer walked in. The lady carefully inspected each of the utensils. Then she held the glasses up to the light. "Waiter," she asked, "how is the fish prepared?"

"Broiled," Mel answered.

"I like mine fried," the lady snapped.

Mel smiled. "We try to please," he said, "and I'm sure the chef will be happy to fry your fish. Would you like to order?"

"No, thank you," said the lady, smiling now. "I'm not really hungry. You see, I just became the owner of this restaurant."

2.   Larry stared at the x-ray machine. He had seen one once at the dentist's office, but he never thought that one would be used on Sam. Sam was wrapped in a blanket and resting quietly in Larry's lap. The veterinarian had given the collie a shot and told Larry that his dog was not in pain. "The x-ray is just to make sure that all is well," he said. "Sam will probably be back chasing cars in a week or so. But you should try to break him of that habit."

3.   Janice looks closely at Howard Ross for a few minutes. At first Howard sits rather stiffly, but then he starts to relax a bit. "Now," thinks Janice, "he looks more natural." Janice looks at his face until she understands its shape. She studies the way the light plays on his skin, making patterns of lights and shadows. She studies the color of his hair, his eyes, and his skin. Only then does she turn to pick up a brush and dip it into the oil paints.

4.   Wendy stared at the unfinished science report. It was due tomorrow, and there were hours of work to do on it. "I don't mind working," Wendy thought, "but the game is tomorrow." She picked up the phone to call her soccer coach. She could imagine what he would say: "You know the rule. It's up to you." Wendy knew the rule. Missing practice meant not playing the next game. But it was her fault that the report hadn't been completed. She straightened her back as she heard the coach answer the phone.

5.   Rachel kept her one spare house key hidden under a rock in the garden. Then if the keys in her handbag were ever lost, she'd be able to get back into her own house. Coming home late one night, Rachel realized that she'd forgotten to put the keys back in her handbag. She had left her keys at work! Sighing with weariness, she got her spare house key from under the rock, let herself into the house, and fell into bed. Several days later, Rachel's handbag was stolen. When she returned home and looked under the rock for her spare key, it wasn't there.

IDENTIFYING INFERENCES

			T	F	I
1.	(A)	The customer examined the restaurant's tableware.	☒	☐	☐
	(B)	The customer said she liked her fish baked.	☐	☒	☐
	(C)	Mel insisted that only broiled fish could be served.	☐	☒	☐
	(D)	The new owner was pleased with Mel's reply.	☐	☐	☒

			T	F	I
2.	(A)	The dog was suffering pain.	☐	☐	☐
	(B)	Larry had never seen an x-ray machine before.	☐	☐	☐
	(C)	Larry's dog, Sam, had been hit by a car.	☐	☐	☐
	(D)	Sam was wrapped in a blanket.	☐	☐	☐

			T	F	I
3.	(A)	Howard Ross grows more tense the longer he sits.	☐	☐	☐
	(B)	Janice observes her subject very carefully.	☐	☐	☐
	(C)	Janice uses pastel chalk for her work.	☐	☐	☐
	(D)	Janice will paint Howard's portrait.	☐	☐	☐

			T	F	I
4.	(A)	Wendy was working on a science report.	☐	☐	☐
	(B)	Wendy was aware of the rule about missing practice.	☐	☐	☐
	(C)	Wendy decided to miss practice to finish the report.	☐	☐	☐
	(D)	Wendy heard the coach's wife answer the phone.	☐	☐	☐

			T	F	I
5.	(A)	Rachel kept her only spare house key hidden under the doormat.	☐	☐	☐
	(B)	When Rachel had left her keys at work, she found the house key under the rock.	☐	☐	☐
	(C)	After Rachel's purse had been stolen, she found the house key under the rock.	☐	☐	☐
	(D)	Rachel had forgotten to replace her house key under the rock.	☐	☐	☐

DETECTING THE SEQUENCE

Read the story. As you read it, look for clues that let you know the order in which things happened. Then, on the opposite page, circle the letter choice that best answers the question about the sequence of events.

Adventurous Nellie Bly

Reading the *Pittsburgh Dispatch* one day, Elizabeth Cochrane was upset by an editorial. It seemed to say that women were not the equals of men. Cochrane fired off an angry reply. The *Dispatch*'s editors were so impressed by the teenager's writing that they offered her a job.

Elizabeth Cochrane soon became a star at the *Pittsburgh Dispatch.* Then she took on the pen name Nellie Bly and wrote many newspaper articles. Her stories about poor living conditions in Pittsburgh were widely read. Businesses who advertised in the *Dispatch* were unhappy with the articles, however. They asked the paper to send Bly on vacation. She went to Mexico and began writing about conditions there. Soon the Mexican government also asked her to leave.

Then Nellie Bly moved on to New York City. She joined the staff of the *New York World,* where she quickly made a name for herself. No adventure was too great for Bly. First, she posed as an immigrant worker to expose dishonest hiring agencies. Next, she arranged to get arrested on false theft charges. Then Bly wrote articles about the terrible conditions she found in prison. Once she jumped off a ferry to see how quickly its rescue crew responded.

In 1889, Bly set out on her greatest adventure. Sixteen years before, Jules Verne's novel *Around the World in Eighty Days* had been published. The book described an eighty-day balloon trip around the world. Bly said she could beat that imaginary record. She set out from New York on November 14, 1889. After crossing the Atlantic, Bly stopped in France. There she interviewed the book's author, Jules Verne. She went on to Egypt, India, China, and Japan, and then crossed the Pacific to San Francisco. Bly raced across the United States toward New Jersey, just across the river from New York. Meanwhile, readers of the *New York World* eagerly followed her journey.

Seventy-two days and six hours after she left, Bly arrived in Jersey City. Cannons boomed, whistles sounded, and crowds cheered. Nellie Bly waved happily, knowing she had beaten more than the clock. She had proved that women can do almost anything.

DETECTING THE SEQUENCE

1. **Which of these events happened first?**

    (A) The *Pittsburgh Dispatch* hired Elizabeth Cochrane.

    (B) Cochrane read an editorial in the *Pittsburgh Dispatch*.

    (C) Cochrane wrote an angry letter to the *Dispatch*.

    (D) Cochrane became a star at the *Pittsburgh Dispatch*.

2. **Which of these events happened last?**

    (A) Bly arrived in Jersey City.

    (B) Bly interviewed Jules Verne.

    (C) Bly set out from New York.

    (D) Bly crossed the Pacific to San Francisco.

3. **When did businesses that advertised in the *Dispatch* ask the paper to send Bly on vacation?**

    (A) while she wrote articles about conditions in Mexico

    (B) after she wrote about living conditions in Pittsburgh

    (C) when the *Dispatch*'s editors offered her a job

    (D) after she moved to New York City

4. **What did Nellie Bly do just after she moved to New York City?**

    (A) She went to Mexico on vacation.

    (B) She took the pen name Nellie Bly.

    (C) She joined the staff of the *New York World*.

    (D) She set off on a trip around the world.

5. **Which took place 16 years before Nellie Bly set out to circle the world?**

    (A) *Around the World in Eighty Days* was published.

    (B) Bly interviewed Jules Verne.

    (C) *New York World* readers followed Bly's journey.

    (D) Bly raced across the United States.

PROGRESS CHECK

Exploring Language

To supply the missing word in an analogy, draw a conclusion about the relationship between the words in the complete pair. Then supply a word that has the same relationship to the remaining word. Remember that the relationship between the words in each pair must be similar, and the items in each pair must be in the same order.

Read each of the following incomplete analogies. Write the word that correctly completes each analogy.

1. **Valuable** is to **precious** as **worthless** is to _____ .

2. **Poodle** is to _____ as **Siamese** is to **cat**.

3. _____ is to **firefighter** as **hammer** is to **carpenter**.

4. **Numbers** are to **mathematics** as _____ are to **language**.

5. **Above** is to _____ as **front** is to **back**.

6. **Strings** are to **guitar** as _____ are to **piano**.

7. **Flock** is to **geese** as _____ is to **horses**.

8. _____ is to **state** as **state** is to **country**.

9. **Fawn** is to **deer** as _____ is to **cow**.

10. **Rainbow trout** is to _____ as **eagle** is to **bird**.

Expressing Yourself

Choose one of these activities. Use another piece of paper for your responses.

1. Create your own analogies based on your favorite television or story characters, athletes, or entertainers from television, music, or movies. Share your analogies. Be sure you can explain the relationships within the analogies.

2. Write an analogy of your own based on each kind of relationship listed below. Look back at analogies at the top of the page for examples if you need help.
   1. antonyms
   2. item to category
   3. part to whole
   4. synonyms
   5. animal to its young

PROGRESS CHECK

Exploring Language

Let's see how good you are at drawing conclusions based on just three facts! Read each of the following items. Based on the overheard bits of conversation, tell what is happening.

1. "Get those ladders up there!" "Hoses on!" "There are people on the top floor!"

   _____

2. "It's almost time for the show to start." "Look at that line at the ticket booth!" "Do you want to get some popcorn?"

   _____

3. "The Flying Estradas will now perform their own version of the triple somersault!" "Drum roll, please!" "He's going to fall! Oh, I can't bear to watch!"

   _____

4. "Forty-second Street. This station is Forty-second Street." "Excuse me. Coming through." "Watch your step, please, and stay clear of the track."

   _____

5. "Please deposit 25 cents for the next three minutes." "Operator, I have no more change!" "This is a recording."

   _____

6. "Come, Sandy." "Exercise over. You can praise your dog now." "Good boy, Sandy!"

   _____

7. "Look! Bases loaded!" "How many outs?" "Maybe she'll hit a grand slam homer!"

   _____

8. "Open your test booklets and begin." "Answer all the questions." "No talking!"

   _____

FOLLOWING DIRECTIONS

Read each set of directions, then circle the letter choice that best answers the question about the directions.

DIRECTIONS: There are several things you can use for a container; a fishbowl, a candy jar, or a big glass are good choices. The most suitable plants for your terrarium are small woodland growths, but any tropical flowers will do. After choosing your plants, plan the arrangement on a piece of paper. Next place coarse stone and charcoal in the bottom of your container. Add two inches of moist soil. Arrange your plants in the soil as you have planned. After the planting, use an atomizer to spray the soil with water. Cover the container with a small piece of glass. Place your completed terrarium where there is good light, but not in direct sunlight. This "plant world under glass" will spring to life before you know it.

1. These instructions will help you—

    (A) tend a garden   (B) make paper flowers
    (C) find tropical flowers (D) build a terrarium

2. Before filling the terrarium, you should—

    (A) use an atomizer   (B) plan the plant arrangement
    (C) place it in good light (D) cover the container

3. The moist soil should be added after—

    (A) you use the atomizer (B) the cover is removed
    (C) the stone and charcoal (D) the terrarium is covered

4. After spraying the soil, you should—

    (A) add more dirt   (B) add the charcoal
    (C) arrange the plants (D) cover the container

38

USING THE CONTEXT

Read each set of sentences. In each set of sentences, there are two blanks. Circle the letter choice for the correct word that goes in each blank.

Do you ever ask someone to "hang loose"? If you do, you want the person to be more calm, unworried, and (1) _____ . This expression originated back in 1950. It is the (2) _____ of being hung up, which means being in a state of nervous tension.

1. **(A) relaxed**   **(B) irritated**   **(C) ignorant**   **(D) isolated**
2. **(A) identical**   **(B) opposite**   **(C) illustration** **(D) pursuit**

Can loud noises harm your health? To find out, scientists subjected rats to loud and frequent noise. Examinations showed that they acted very much like humans undergoing a (3) _____ (4) _____ . They developed ulcers, lost their appetites, and found it difficult to make decisions.

3. **(A) contagious**   **(B) healthy**   **(C) nervous**   **(D) medical**
4. **(A) examination** **(B) buildup**   **(C) breakdown**   **(D) operation**

After the *Titanic* was sent to the bottom of the sea by an iceberg in 1912, the Ice Patrol was founded. The patrol charts the (5) _____ of bergs in the North Atlantic. While the patrol has been active, not a single (6) _____ has been lost because of icebergs.

5. **(A) size**   **(B) history**   **(C) movements**   **(D) temperature**
6. **(A) record**   **(B) day**   **(C) raft**   **(D) life**

The chalk used to write on the board at school is actually gypsum. Chalk would (7) _____ too easily to be effective. Real chalk is used in (8) _____ that scour and polish. It also is widely used in a cleansing agent known to all of us—toothpaste.

7. **(A) harden**   **(B) burn**   **(C) crumble**   **(D) meet**
8. **(A) gargles**   **(B) powders**   **(C) acids**   **(D) bleaches**

It is a common belief that a very cold winter follows an unusually hot summer. Weather experts say there is no evidence for this belief. If a summer has been hotter than usual, the winter that follows seems (9) _____ than (10) _____ .

9. **(A) wetter**   **(B) longer**   **(C) colder**   **(D) milder**
10. **(A) winter**   **(B) usual**   **(C) spring**   **(D) frost**

GETTING THE MAIN IDEA

Read the stories, then, on the opposite page, circle the letter choice for the sentence that tells the main idea of the story.

1. What do you think is the most popular soda flavor in the United States? If you thought of cola, you are right. Almost two out of every three cans or bottles of soda that are sold are cola. The second most popular flavor is lemon-lime, but that is far behind cola. Orange, ginger ale, grape, and root beer are next down the list.

2. Electric companies may put a special "clock" in everyone's kitchen soon. Numbers flash on the screen of this "clock," telling how much electricity is being used in the home at the moment and how much the monthly electric bill is to that moment. Electric companies think people will use less electricity if they realize how much it is costing them.

3. Art in its many forms has built a bridge between our civilization and the cultures that preceded it. Pictures on pottery have revealed many aspects of the life and times of people of particular eras. The painter has pictured civilizations that once flourished and died. Music and dancing also reflect the characters and emotions of our ancestors.

4. Among those who guard the city of Philadelphia are thirty-five chickens. The birds are kept by Philadelphia's Health Department to help assure that no deadly disease strikes the city. Each summer the birds are allowed to be bitten by mosquitoes that fly around the city. The medical workers test the chickens' blood. If the blood contains no disease germs, doctors know the mosquitoes are harmless.

5. A buffalo stampede was a frightening thing to see. The shaggy-headed buffalo, each weighing from one to two thousand pounds, rushed forward, heads low, smashing, trampling, and destroying everything in their way. Their sharp hoofs kicked up dust as they rushed blindly forward, bringing death and destruction to anyone and anything unlucky enough to be caught in their path.

GETTING THE MAIN IDEA

1. The paragraph tells mainly—

   (A) how far behind cola lemon-lime is

   (B) why Americans prefer cola

   (C) what soda flavors Americans prefer

   (D) which nation drinks the most soda

2. The paragraph tells mainly—

   (A) when the special "clock" will operate

   (B) where the special "clock" will be

   (C) whom the special "clock" will be for

   (D) what the special "clock" will do

3. The paragraph tells mainly—

   (A) why artists like history

   (B) how music and dancing reveal the past

   (C) how people learn about themselves

   (D) how various art forms help people learn history

4. The paragraph tells mainly—

   (A) how birds protect a city

   (B) how mosquitoes infect birds

   (C) how mosquitoes carry diseases

   (D) how the Health Department thought of using chickens

5. The paragraph tells mainly—

   (A) how heavy buffalo are

   (B) what a buffalo stampede was like

   (C) how hard buffalo charge

   (D) why people are afraid of some animals

DRAWING CONCLUSIONS

Read the short stories, then, on the opposite page, circle the letter choice that describes something you can tell from the information in the story. Use clues in each story to draw a conclusion to find the correct answer.

1. Ships that carry freight but do not travel on regular runs are called "tramps." A tramp steamer has no fixed schedule. It wanders from port to port. Declining in numbers in recent years, tramp steamers are less and less often seen. When the last of the tramp steamers has made its final port call, a little of the romance of the old sailing days will have vanished.

2. The rhinoceros is regarded by hunters as one of the most dangerous animals in the world. Despite its size, the animal gallops along at twenty-five to thirty-five miles an hour. Its horn gives it a formidable weapon. What is worse, the rhino has a mean temper. Without any apparent reason, the tanklike creature will attack even a railroad train!

3. Elephants display surprising intelligence. In the London Zoo elephants were separated from the public by two fences. Sometimes peanuts thrown by the onlookers landed between these fences, beyond the reach of both the people and the elephants. With a blast of air from their trunks, the elephants simply blew the peanuts back to the crowd so they could be tossed back again!

4. The English language did not originate in England. The language that became known as English was apparently first spoken by people living in what is now Germany. Tribes from this area brought their language with them when they invaded England. When we hear this early English, known as Anglo-Saxon or Old English, we find it hard to believe that it was the ancestor of Modern English. It sounds more like German.

5. The flu, or influenza, has been around for centuries. Its name reminds us that people once looked to the sky for its cause. The word *influenza* comes from the Italian word for *influence,* because people blamed their aches and fevers on the influence of the stars. In modern times, scientists have found a better explanation by looking through a microscope. The flu is caused by a tiny form of matter called a virus.

DRAWING CONCLUSIONS

1. You can tell that the writer thinks that—

   (A) there will always be some tramp steamers

   (B) the end of tramp steamers is no loss

   (C) tramp steamers should have a schedule

   (D) tramp steamers will one day be no more

2. The story gives—

   (A) ten reasons why hunters fear the rhino

   (B) at least three reasons why the rhino is dangerous

   (C) the reason for the rhino's mean temper

   (D) a complete list of the rhino's habits

3. From the story you cannot tell—

   (A) where the elephants were kept

   (B) how many fences were there

   (C) how many peanuts were lost

   (D) how the elephants returned the peanuts

4. The writer suggests that without Germany—

   (A) there would be no written language

   (B) the English language would be different today

   (C) there would be no English people

   (D) England would have no language

5. From the story you can tell that—

   (A) a virus can be seen with the naked eye

   (B) the stars once caused sickness

   (C) the author believes in scientific explanations

   (D) a cure for the flu has been discovered

IDENTIFYING INFERENCES

Read the short stories. On the opposite page, read the sentences about each story. Decide whether each sentence is true (**T**), false (**F**), or an inference (**I**). A true sentence tells a fact from the story. A false sentence tells something that is not true. An inference says something that is *probably* true, based on facts in the story. More than one sentence about each story may be true, false, or an inference. Place an X in the correct box to mark your answer.

1.   Coleman trudged down the street, his bat thrown over his shoulder and his cap pulled down over his eyes. Dirt stains covered every inch of his uniform. He looked straight ahead, ignoring his friends who waved to him from the park. As he approached the house, his mother looked out the kitchen window. Just then Coleman lifted the bat over his shoulder and slammed it into the ground. Mrs. Nelson was surprised at her son's action.

2.   Gwendolyn felt nervous as, from her position backstage, she watched her classmates perform. She had expected to be a little scared, but she had not thought she would feel such a mass of butterflies in her stomach. Mr. Kanu had given the whole class a lecture about opening-night jitters. He explained that people always feel nervous the first time they perform in front of an audience. "Wow! Was he right!" thought Gwendolyn. "I think I'll practice my lines one more time."

3.   Sam knew how easy it was to let homework slide. He had a habit of waiting until just before bedtime to start his work. This meant that he was often too tired to concentrate on his assignments. "Maybe my teacher can help me organize my afterschool time the way he encouraged my friend, Donna, to work out a schedule," thought Sam. "If I do my homework immediately after school, maybe I'll do a better job." Sam decided to tell Mr. Needleman his idea. Sam was sure Mr. Needleman would have more good suggestions for getting the homework done.

4.   Warren, now in his senior year, had studied very hard for the final math test. He had decided to work as hard as he could all month in order to get an A in math on his report card. Warren's father had helped him study. He had explained some formulas that Warren did not understand, and had also made up extra problems for Warren to work on. "The extra work really paid off," thought Warren. "I knew how to solve all the questions on the test. I'll bet I didn't make any mistakes at all."

5.   "What's wrong with you?" asked Lloyd. "You look depressed."

"I *am* depressed," replied Teddy forlornly. "Mother won't let me start a yard-cleaning service. My friend Alvin and I had a great idea for making money. We were going to put an advertisement in the paper telling people about our new service. Then they would hire us to take care of their yards."

"Matt Johnson has that kind of business," said Lloyd, "but he's much older than you."

IDENTIFYING INFERENCES

			T	F	I
1.	(A)	Coleman's friends waved to him.	☒	☐	☐
	(B)	Coleman was upset over the baseball game he had just played in.	☐	☐	☒
	(C)	Mrs. Nelson was surprised to see Coleman throw down his bat.	☒	☐	☐
	(D)	Coleman's uniform was spotless.	☐	☒	☐

			T	F	I
2.	(A)	Gwendolyn was worried that her nervousness would cause her to forget her part.	☐	☐	☐
	(B)	Mr. Kanu knows that stage fright is to be expected.	☐	☐	☐
	(C)	Gwendolyn was the first performer to go onstage.	☐	☐	☐
	(D)	Gwendolyn disagreed with what Mr. Kanu had said about opening-night jitters.	☐	☐	☐

			T	F	I
3.	(A)	Mr. Needleman has a reputation for helping his students.	☐	☐	☐
	(B)	Donna was Sam's friend.	☐	☐	☐
	(C)	Sam was often too tired to give full attention to his studies.	☐	☐	☐
	(D)	Donna had gotten no help from Mr. Needleman.	☐	☐	☐

			T	F	I
4.	(A)	Warren had done a lot of extra studying in math.	☐	☐	☐
	(B)	Warren was in his senior year.	☐	☐	☐
	(C)	Warren is going to get his *A* in math.	☐	☐	☐
	(D)	Warren's father couldn't understand the formulas.	☐	☐	☐

			T	F	I
5.	(A)	Teddy's mother wanted Alvin and Teddy to start a yard-cleaning business.	☐	☐	☐
	(B)	Teddy and Alvin wanted to put an ad in the paper.	☐	☐	☐
	(C)	Matt Johnson has a yard-cleaning business.	☐	☐	☐
	(D)	Lloyd thought that Teddy and Alvin were too young to start a yard-cleaning service.	☐	☐	☐

GETTING THE FACTS

Read the story, then, on the opposite page, circle the letter choice that best completes each sentence about the story.

Escape

"We're going to escape," said William Craft to his wife, Ellen. They had just witnessed another slave being flogged to death at the whipping post. From Macon, Georgia, they would have to flee a thousand miles north to reach freedom—but William had a plan!

They would escape by train while slave catchers searched for them in swamps. "You will dress as a young male planter," William chuckled. He drew a silk hat, a waistcoat, and trousers from a bag. Ellen's skin color was so fair that she had often been mistaken for white. "I will be your slave," William explained. "Just try to speak as little as possible," he cautioned.

On December 21, 1848, Ellen purchased tickets for herself and her "slave." Once on the train, Ellen was stunned. Beside her sat one of the most dreaded slave catchers—Willis Hughes. Hughes and another slave catcher, after getting off, recognized Ellen through the window. For the moment, however, the fugitives were safe. The train was speeding away.

They stayed at the finest hotel in Charleston, South Carolina. Everyone treated Ellen with great respect. She was the very image of a typical planter. The manager did not even ask her to register. William had put her arm in a sling because neither he nor Ellen had ever been taught to write.

The next morning the slave catchers arrived in Charleston, but William and Ellen were safely aboard the train. Only four more days to Baltimore, Maryland, the last stop before freedom! However, in Baltimore the ticket agent told Ellen she could not take her slave North without ownership papers.

Suddenly William had an inspiration. "I am taking young master to a doctor in Philadelphia," he explained. "Young master is sick."

At that moment another passenger said, "I know the young man. I have come with him all the way from Georgia." The agent let them go.

Ellen and William boarded the train to Philadelphia, Pennsylvania, and freedom. It was one of the most daring of all escapes from slavery.

GETTING THE FACTS

1. Ellen and William lived in the area of—
   - (A) **Mobile, Alabama**
   - (B) **Miami, Florida**
   - (C) **Macon, Georgia**
   - (D) **Atlanta, Georgia**

2. Freedom lay at a distance of—
   - (A) **1,000 miles**
   - (B) **2,000 miles**
   - (C) **900 miles**
   - (D) **500 miles**

3. Ellen was to dress as a young male—
   - (A) **slave**
   - (B) **ticket agent**
   - (C) **manager**
   - (D) **planter**

4. Ellen purchased train tickets on—
   - (A) **January 5, 1959**
   - (B) **December 21, 1848**
   - (C) **May 20, 1789**
   - (D) **November 30, 1821**

5. The man who sat beside Ellen was named—
   - (A) **Moore**
   - (B) **Carroll**
   - (C) **Hughes**
   - (D) **Smith**

6. They stayed at the finest hotel in—
   - (A) **Philadelphia**
   - (B) **Macon**
   - (C) **Baltimore**
   - (D) **Charleston**

7. Ellen's arm was in a—
   - (A) **cast**
   - (B) **sling**
   - (C) **sleeve**
   - (D) **bandage**

8. The slave catchers arrived in Charleston—
   - (A) **the next morning**
   - (B) **the next afternoon**
   - (C) **that evening**
   - (D) **two days later**

9. The ticket agent demanded—
   - (A) **money**
   - (B) **papers**
   - (C) **tickets**
   - (D) **passengers**

10. William announced he was taking Ellen to a—
    - (A) **friend**
    - (B) **hospital**
    - (C) **doctor**
    - (D) **relative**

GETTING THE MAIN IDEA

Read the stories, then, on the opposite page, circle the letter choice for the sentence that tells the main idea of the story.

---

1.   Texas longhorns were not like the gentle, fat, slow-moving cattle of today. They were huge—weighing over a thousand pounds—and were almost as fast as deer. They had a fighting spirit, pointed horns that they enjoyed tossing, sharp hooves, and a deep dislike for anything in their way. The Texas longhorns were fierce animals that commanded respect from people—and even from grizzly bears!

---

2.   Few people are aware of the huge size of Canada. It is the second largest country in the world. Only the Soviet Union is larger. Canada reaches one-fourth of the way around the world. It has more lakes than the rest of the world's countries combined. Yet there are but 24 million people in this vast land, only about as many as in the state of California.

---

3.   The Haskell Opera House lies partly in the United States, partly in Canada. The entrance is in America, but the stage is in Canada. Local people tell about a man wanted by the American police. He was discovered performing on the stage of the Haskell Opera House. Since he stayed in the Canadian half of the building, and so was in a foreign country, American authorities couldn't arrest him!

---

4.   Canada is more than a land of great beauty. It is also a land of vast forests. Lumber and the products that come from lumber make Canada a leader in world paper production. The pulp and paper industry continues to grow and is now Canada's leading industry.

---

5.   Communication means a sharing of information. People communicate with each other in many ways. Much communication is face-to-face and silent. People smile and laugh. They shake hands. They wave. They squeeze a friend's hand to communicate sympathy or greetings. People share information about how they feel, often without as much as a single word.

GETTING THE MAIN IDEA

1. The paragraph tells mainly—
    (A) how big the Texas longhorns were
    (B) what Texas longhorns were like
    (C) why grizzly bears ran away
    (D) what the horns of the Texas longhorns were like

2. The paragraph tells mainly—
    (A) where Canada is located
    (B) why few people live in Canada
    (C) how large Canada is
    (D) how many lakes Canada has

3. The paragraph tells mainly—
    (A) where the Haskell Opera House is located
    (B) why the police wanted to arrest a performer
    (C) what strange event occurred at the Haskell Opera House
    (D) which part of the Haskell Opera House is in America

4. The paragraph tells mainly—
    (A) how many trees there are
    (B) why Canada has so many trees
    (C) what Canada gets from its forests
    (D) why Canada is so beautiful

5. The paragraph tells mainly—
    (A) what information means
    (B) how people communicate without words
    (C) how people show sympathy by squeezing hands
    (D) why words aren't important

FOLLOWING DIRECTIONS

Read each set of directions, then circle the letter choice that best answers the question about the directions.

DIRECTIONS: Relax and don't throw yourself into a panic. Concentrate on how you traveled. Mark a tree on all sides so that you can spot it from any direction. Then walk in a circle around the tree examining the surrounding area. Be sure to leave a note for your fellow hikers, telling them the direction in which you headed. Try to locate a stream. Follow it downstream; it will probably lead you to a town or village. Always look for high ground. Look and call out from a hill or tall tree. Follow telephone wires, power lines, and the sounds of cars; these will lead you to civilization. If possible, send up a smoke signal. Should darkness fall while you are still lost, stay where you are and look for shelter.

1. These directions show you how to—

    (A) **start a camping trip**   (B) **start a fire**

    (C) **climb a tree**   (D) **react if you become lost**

2. Before examining the surrounding ground,—

    (A) **find a stream**   (B) **mark a tree**

    (C) **start a fire**   (D) **find shelter**

3. Should you find a stream, follow it—

    (A) **upstream**   (B) **toward telephone lines**

    (C) **downstream**   (D) **even after dark**

4. If darkness falls and you're still lost,—

    (A) **follow the sound of autos**   (B) **locate a stream**

    (C) **mark a tree**   (D) **stay where you are**

USING THE CONTEXT

Read each set of sentences. In each set of sentences, there are two blanks. Circle the letter choice for the correct word that goes in each blank.

The record cold for the United States was eighty degrees below zero in Prospect Creek, Alaska, in July of 1983. But this (1) _____ was balmy compared to that (2) _____ at Vostok, a Russian Antarctic station. Here the temperatures are the lowest on Earth—with a record low of 128.6 degrees below zero!

1. **(A) thermometer**　　**(B) humidity**　　**(C) temperature**　　**(D) event**
2. **(A) approved**　　**(B) prescribed**　　**(C) caught**　　**(D) registered**

Hurricanes create floods. When these storms move in toward shore, they whip up huge waves. These waves can be highly dangerous. More (3) _____ are caused by (4) _____ than by wind.

3. **(A) deaths**　　**(B) accidents**　　**(C) rescues**　　**(D) bruises**
4. **(A) confusion**　　**(B) lifesaving**　　**(C) drowning**　　**(D) fear**

The common house cat played an important role in winning the West. Rats were (5) _____ grain supplies maintained for the army. In desperation, cats were ordered from the East. The new arrivals kept the rat population under (6) _____ .

5. **(A) routing**　　**(B) harvesting**　　**(C) entering**　　**(D) destroying**
6. **(A) guard**　　**(B) scrutiny**　　**(C) supervision**　　**(D) control**

Transportation is one of the basic needs of people. Its importance can hardly be measured. From earliest times inventive (7) _____ have been seeking to improve the (8) _____ of moving persons and goods from place to place.

7. **(A) tools**　　**(B) minds**　　**(C) clubs**　　**(D) trucks**
8. **(A) methods**　　**(B) differences**　　**(C) belongings**　　**(D) tricks**

Gray or white hair is not caused by worrying or even by aging. People (9) _____ certain genes that determine when and how much gray hair they will get. It can start as early as the teens or whenever the hair glands decrease their (10) _____ of coloring matter.

9. **(A) annex**　　**(B) inherit**　　**(C) revise**　　**(D) vote**
10. **(A) devotion**　　**(B) campaign**　　**(C) production**　　**(D) appointment**

GETTING THE MAIN IDEA

Read the stories, then, on the opposite page, circle the letter choice for the sentence that tells the main idea of the story.

1.   The human body can adapt itself remarkably to difficult conditions of living. For example, people who live high in the Andes Mountains, where the air is very thin, have an extra quart of blood in their bodies to help them get enough oxygen. Also, from years of walking barefoot in the cold, these people have grown extra blood vessels in their feet. They can walk barefoot even in snow without discomfort.

2.   We think of the collie, German shepherd, Great Dane, Newfoundland, and Saint Bernard as fun-loving pets. Once these famous breeds were just work dogs with special duties to perform. The collie and German shepherd were flock tenders. The Great Dane was a property guard. The Newfoundland was the world's champion lifesaver. The Saint Bernard broke trails for people over deep snowfalls in the Alps mountains.

3.   Perhaps the world's most violent snowstorm is the purga. This dreaded blizzard sweeps over northern Siberia in winter. Its violence is so great that people cannot open their eyes. Many people even report difficulty in standing upright. People caught in this blinding storm often become lost and freeze to death within yards of the doorways to their homes.

4.   Ancient papyrus sheets have been discovered in the sands of Egypt. They have been preserved by the dryness of the climate. One sheet contains a laundry list: "fine tunics 2, dalmatics 2, breeches 2, felt slippers 1, carpetbag, ground-sheet, small pillow, etc." A letter sent home by a school child ends with a postscript, "Please feed my pigeons." How like our own were the daily lives of these people!

5.   There is a worm in the sea that is actually a living fishline! This is the fishline worm. It can be found curled up under a rock. It looks small, but when it uncoils it is eighty feet long. The sharp teeth of the worm attach themselves to a small fish. Once they do, they never let go. Finally the fish tires of fighting the long worm. The fishline worm then devours its catch.

GETTING THE MAIN IDEA

1. The paragraph tells mainly—

    (A) how Andean people get cold from walking barefoot

    (B) what the air is like in the Andes

    (C) how people's bodies can adjust to a climate

    (D) how much oxygen everyone's blood needs

2. The paragraph tells mainly—

    (A) which dogs are fun-loving pets

    (B) where some dogs were used to guard property

    (C) why some dogs were used to do work

    (D) how certain pet dogs were once work animals

3. The paragraph tells mainly—

    (A) how often the purga occurs

    (B) what happens in winter

    (C) why people can't open their eyes

    (D) why the purga is dreaded

4. The paragraph tells mainly—

    (A) where papyrus sheets were discovered

    (B) how the papyrus sheets were preserved

    (C) what one school child of ancient Egypt wrote

    (D) what the papyrus sheets reveal

5. The paragraph tells mainly—

    (A) how the worm uncoils

    (B) what kinds of fish are caught

    (C) how fishline worms are caught

    (D) how a worm catches fish

NAME _____

DRAWING CONCLUSIONS

Read the short stories, then, on the opposite page, circle the letter choice that describes something you can tell from the information in the story. Use clues in each story to draw a conclusion to find the correct answer.

1. Long ago, passenger pigeons flew over North America in such vast numbers that they actually darkened the sun as they passed. In a single flock there were often more than a billion passenger pigeons! Single nesting areas were often thirty or more miles long and three to six miles wide. Today, the passenger pigeon is extinct. The last survivor of the breed died in a Cincinnati zoo in 1914.

2. In 1959, a British engineer invented a transportation machine called the hovercraft. It is a boat-shaped, flat-bottomed carrier that rides on a cushion of air created by motors. One special feature of the hovercraft is its ability to ride over both land and water at heights low enough for easy viewing. This has been useful in the exploration of swampy rivers such as the Amazon.

3. The most beautiful of all horses is the Arabian Asil. Its neck is gracefully arched. Its head is small and delicate with eyes that are large, fiery, and far apart. Its small ears point inward. This horse has a full, flowing tail that it carries high, and its skin is a shiny black. The Arabian Asil is one of the most beautiful of all creatures.

4. The area that birds defend against other birds of their own species is called a territory. By controlling such an area, the bird protects its family from other birds of the same species. It also insures both food and nesting materials in this way. The size of the territory depends on many factors, such as the amount of food available, the type of bird, and even its size.

5. Down through the ages flea circuses have been used to attract people to fairs and markets. Fleas are dressed in tiny costumes. Some are tightrope walkers. Others take part in chariot races and tugs of war. Today, most of these circuses have disappeared. However, the name remains in the so-called flea market, an open-air market in which various goods are sold.

DRAWING CONCLUSIONS

1. From the story you cannot tell—

   (A) how large the flocks were

   (B) when the passenger pigeon became extinct

   (C) why the passenger pigeon died out

   (D) where the last passenger pigeon died

2. From the story you can tell that the hovercraft—

   (A) could be used for exploring a chain of islands

   (B) resembles a helicopter

   (C) is unsafe in stormy weather

   (D) creates less noise and pollution than an automobile

3. A good name for the Arabian Asil would be—

   (A) Star of the North

   (B) Brown Eyes

   (C) Speedy

   (D) Black Beauty

4. The story gives—

   (A) ten reasons for bird territories

   (B) the writer's opinion of birds

   (C) three reasons for bird territories

   (D) the size of most bird territories

5. Fleas were helpful in—

   (A) scattering crowds

   (B) drawing crowds

   (C) annoying crowds

   (D) calming crowds

IDENTIFYING INFERENCES

Read the short stories. On the opposite page, read the sentences about each story. Decide whether each sentence is true (**T**), false (**F**), or an inference (**I**). A true sentence tells a fact from the story. A false sentence tells something that is not true. An inference says something that is *probably* true, based on facts in the story. More than one sentence about each story may be true, false, or an inference. Place an X in the correct box to mark your answer.

1.   Candice had paused at the front door for a few seconds, as if hoping to gain entrance. Her shiny black hair glistened in the sun. Her wide-open green eyes gazed around expectantly. Then she turned and began walking very slowly away from the house. She stopped a moment to stretch her legs and back.

      "Are you hungry?" asked the boy in the house, opening the door. "Come on, I'll give you something to eat."

      Without saying a word in reply, Candice bounded into the house and headed straight for the kitchen. A fish dinner and some warm milk awaited her.

2.   Jeannie broke the surface of the water with a gasp. She spotted the judges on the shore and began stroking steadily toward them. As she raised her head to inhale, she caught glimpses of Nell and Cheryl. Nell was several yards behind her, but Cheryl was even with her. "Should I make the push now," thought Jeannie, "or wait until the last ten yards?" Jeannie remembered that Cheryl often lost strength during the last quarter of a race—which was right about now. "Here I go!" exclaimed Jeannie.

3.   "What will you get Mom for her birthday?" Eddie asked Monica.

      "I've been thinking about getting her some new gardening tools," said Monica. "The ones she has are all bent and rusty."

      "Well, if we went in together on a present, suggested Eddie, "we could get her what she really wants and needs."

      "What's that?" asked Monica.

      "A gas lawn mower," replied Eddie. "You know how she knocks herself out pushing that old hand mower around the yard."

      "Great idea!" agreed Monica.

4.   "I wonder why they're building that skyscraper backwards?" said Mr. Heath. "It doesn't seem logical to complete it from the top down."

      "I read a brief news article about that new building method," said Mrs. Drew. "First they build the frame. Then they hang the outer skin of the building on the frame from the top down. The outside of the building comes in sections. Each section has hooks that let it hang on the frame."

      "That's very interesting," said Mr. Heath. "Do they always begin hanging the sections from the top, or could they start anywhere?"

      "I've no idea," said Mrs. Drew. "I've told all I know about it."

5.   Jennifer's father hammered in the last stake and looked doubtfully at the tent. "I see we have another small tear in the side. I'd better fix it right now. No telling if we might have a little rain tonight."

      "Will the tent be all right, Dad?" asked Jennifer.

      "Oh, sure, but we'll retire 'old faithful' here after this camping trip and get a new one for next summer."

IDENTIFYING INFERENCES

Read the passages below. On the basis of the information presented in each passage, decide whether each of the statements that follows the passage is true (T), false (F), or inferred (I) from the passage.

			T	F	I
1.	(A)	Candice is a cat.			☒
	(B)	The boy gave Candice a fish dinner and some warm milk.	☒		
	(C)	Candice turned and walked away from the house after the boy called her.		☒	
	(D)	Candice had eaten at the boy's house before.			☒

			T	F	I
2.	(A)	Jeannie had a good chance of winning the race.			
	(B)	Jeannie was several yards ahead of Nell.			
	(C)	Cheryl always sped up during the last quarter.			
	(D)	Jeannie didn't think Nell would win the race.			

			T	F	I
3.	(A)	Monica had been thinking about getting her mother some gardening tools.			
	(B)	Eddie wanted to get the old hand mower sharpened.			
	(C)	Mother's present gardening tools are rusty.			
	(D)	Mother prefers useful presents to impractical gifts.			

			T	F	I
4.	(A)	Mrs. Drew told Mr. Heath what she knew about the building method.			
	(B)	The news article hadn't given full details of the new method.			
	(C)	Mr. Heath wondered why the builders were constructing the skyscraper backwards.			
	(D)	Mr. Heath wasn't interested in the building method.			

			T	F	I
5.	(A)	Jennifer wondered if the tent would be all right.			
	(B)	The tent had a small tear in the side.			
	(C)	The family had been camping often before.			
	(D)	Jennifer's father referred to the tent as "old ironsides."			

DETECTING THE SEQUENCE

Read the story. As you read it, look for clues that let you know the order in which things happened. Then, on the opposite page, circle the letter choice that best answers the question about the sequence of events.

Mount St. Helens' Eruption

At 8:32 A.M. on May 18, 1980, an earthquake ripped through Mount St. Helens. The north side of the mountain slid away in the quake, and tons of earth crashed down the slope toward the North Toutle River. Meanwhile, gases exploded out of the mountain. Two hundred miles away, people heard the roar. A powerful wave of gas and steam rolled through the sky at the speed of a plane, leveling two hundred square miles of trees. Next came a fiery blanket of ash and a hail of ice and rocks. The ash turned the sky gray and spread over a huge area. All this happened within minutes.

This force of the eruption of Mount St. Helens took even scientists by surprise. They had been watching the Washington mountain since March 21, 1980, when earthquakes had begun shaking it. Scientists had long known that this volcano might erupt. As far back as 1831, it had begun to spew forth different combinations of steam, ash, mud, and lava. These eruptions had continued for twenty-five years. Mount St. Helens then sat quietly for over 120 years. However, a number of geologists predicted an eruption in the twentieth century.

Reporters and geologists hurried to Mount St. Helens after the earthquakes began in March 1980. However, the mountain stayed fairly quiet through April. A second crater appeared near one already there. Then the two blended into one large bowl, which measured 1,700 feet across and 850 feet deep. By May 10, the volcano's activity had increased, and a large bulge formed on its north face. The bulge grew by five feet a day. Scientists expected an eruption soon, but they had no idea it would come with such magnitude and speed.

The eruption on May 18 damaged a vast area. The earth that slid down Mount St. Helens' north slope finally came to rest in the North Toutle Valley, covering the valley with mud and water. The cloud of ash lasted longer and spread much farther. It left inches of choking ash on towns near Mount St. Helens. Soon wind transported the ash cloud east, and within three days it had crossed North America.

Another major eruption of Mount St. Helens is unlikely for thousands of years. Other mountains nearby have showed signs of activity, though. In July 1980, more than fifty small quakes shook Mount Hood. Scientists continue to keep close watch. As they learned from Mount St. Helens, nature's force should not be taken lightly.

DETECTING THE SEQUENCE

1. **Which of these events happened first?**

   (A) Mount St. Helens began spewing forth combinations of steam, ash, mud, and lava.

   (B) An earthquake ripped through Mount St. Helens.

   (C) Reporters and geologists hurried to Mount St. Helens.

   (D) The north side of the mountain slid away, sending tons of earth crashing downward.

2. **Which of these events happened last?**

   (A) Earth from the volcano came to rest in the North Toutle Valley.

   (B) Wind transported the ash cloud east.

   (C) More than fifty small quakes shook Mount Hood.

   (D) A bulge formed on the north face of Mount St. Helens.

3. **What happened at the same time tons of earth crashed down the slope of Mount St. Helens?**

   (A) A hail of ice and rocks fell.

   (B) Gases exploded out of the mountain.

   (C) A second crater appeared on the slope.

   (D) A bulge formed on the north face.

4. **What happened after a blanket of ash came from the mountain?**

   (A) The sky turned gray.

   (B) An earthquake shook the mountain.

   (C) Gas and steam rolled through the sky.

   (D) Reporters and geologists hurried to the mountain.

5. **When did a large bulge form on the face of Mount St. Helens?**

   (A) after the north face slid away

   (B) before a second crater appeared

   (C) while an eruption took place

   (D) after earthquakes began shaking the mountain

IDENTIFYING INFERENCES

Read the short stories. On the opposite page, read the sentences about each story. Decide whether each sentence is true (**T**), false (**F**), or an inference (**I**). A true sentence tells a fact from the story. A false sentence tells something that is not true. An inference says something that is *probably* true, based on facts in the story. More than one sentence about each story may be true, false, or an inference. Place an X in the correct box to mark your answer.

---

1. "What do you think about the announcement the President made last night?" Joe asked his friend, Hank.
    "What announcement?" Hank asked. "I haven't heard anything about it."
    Joe was surprised. "Are you serious? It was the main news in the papers and on the radio this morning."
    "Oh, really? It must be quite important. I'll bet you had a chance to hear the final score of the hockey game on the news, too. How did it turn out?"

---

2. "I'm going to sign up for the CPR class today," Nancy told Rachel.
    "What's CPR?" Rachel wanted to know.
    "Cardiopulmonary resuscitation," said Nancy. "It's emergency treatment for someone who can't breathe. A person having a heart attack needs it. Don't you remember when Jean's father had a heart attack, and she saved his life because she knew how to do CPR? Well, I've been wanting to learn ever since then."

---

3. "As you all know," stated Coach Hanks of the Bears, "this is our last game of the season. We've waited a long time to play the Cougars again, so let's go onto that field and give it all we've got!"
    "Don't worry, Coach Hanks," yelled Tom. "This time the Bears will be on the winning side, and the Cougars will be on the losing side. No more second-place finishes for us!"

---

4. Tony and his parents had sat patiently through all the greetings and announcements on the program. Tony had hardly paid attention while the names of the second- and third-place winners were announced. Tony suddenly sat up straight, though, when he heard the president of the service club say, "And now, ladies and gentlemen, it is my honor to present the grand prize." The president paused a moment and cleared her throat. As she made the announcement, a smile broke out on Tony's face.

---

5. Dana shifted in the saddle and looked at the time. They'd been riding for two hours. "Are we almost there?" Dana called to Fran.
    "It won't be long now," said Fran encouragingly. "The ranch is just over that rise, to the left of that clump of cactuses. And there's a water tank ahead, where we can rest in the shade and have some cool water."

IDENTIFYING INFERENCES

			T	F	I
1.	(A)	Hank is interested more in sports news than in political news.			☒
	(B)	Joe asked Hank his opinion of the President's announcement.	☒		
	(C)	Hank said he hadn't heard about the President's announcement.	☒		
	(D)	Hank was interested in learning how the tennis match had turned out.		☒	

			T	F	I
2.	(A)	Jean had saved her father's life with CPR.			
	(B)	Rachel wanted to know what CPR is.			
	(C)	Nancy said that CPR is emergency treatment for someone who can't breathe.			
	(D)	Nancy likes to be prepared for emergencies.			

			T	F	I
3.	(A)	Tom is on the Bears' team.			
	(B)	This is the Bears' first game of the season.			
	(C)	Tom's team is playing in a championship game.			
	(D)	Tom told the coach not to worry.			

			T	F	I
4.	(A)	Tony was the winner of the grand prize.			
	(B)	The president cleared her throat before announcing the winner of the grand prize.			
	(C)	Tony's parents were at the program.			
	(D)	The second- and third-place winners were announced last.			

			T	F	I
5.	(A)	Fran said there was a water tank ahead.			
	(B)	The ranch is in the desert.			
	(C)	Dana was getting tired of riding.			
	(D)	Dana and Fran had been riding for ten hours.			

PROGRESS CHECK

Exercising Your Skill

A **conclusion** is a decision or judgment you make that is based on facts and information. **Syllogisms** help organize information so that readers can draw a conclusion based on facts. In a syllogism, all the information you need to draw a conclusion is given in two statements called **premises.** Read the two syllogisms below. Note the underlined words and the letters above them. Think about the premises in each syllogism. The first syllogism is correct; the second is incorrect.

	Syllogism 1	Syllogism 2
	A B	A B
First premise:	All horses eat hay.	All horses eat hay.
	C A	C B
Second premise:	Jingle is a horse.	A deer eats hay.
	C B	C A
Conclusion:	Jingle eats hay.	A deer is a horse.

The pattern AB, CA, CB and thinking about the premises will help you recognize a correct syllogism.

Now read each of the following syllogisms. Write *correct* if the syllogism is correct and *incorrect* if it is incorrect.

1. First premise: All tarantulas are spiders.
   Second premise: All spiders have eight legs.
   Conclusion: Tarantulas have eight legs.
   correct

2. First premise: All languages have meaning.
   Second premise: The Russian language has meaning.
   Conclusion: All languages are Russian.

   _____

3. First premise: All snakes shed their skin.
   Second premise: A boa constrictor is a snake.
   Conclusion: A boa constrictor sheds its skin.

PROGRESS CHECK

Exploring Language

Read each of the following syllogisms. For each pair of premises, write a conclusion.

1. First premise: All cats have whiskers.
   Second premise: A lion is a kind of cat.
   Conclusion: _A lion has whiskers._____

2. First premise: All citrus fruits contain vitamin C.
   Second premise: An orange is a citrus fruit.
   Conclusion: _____

3. First premise: Only a native-born American can become president of the United States.
   Second premise: Ronald Reagan was president of the United States from 1981 to 1989.
   Conclusion: _____

4. First premise: All reference books give factual information.
   Second premise: An encyclopedia is a reference book.
   Conclusion: _____

5. First premise: Only living things can breathe.
   Second premise: A rock is not a living thing.
   Conclusion: _____

NAME _____

USING THE CONTEXT

Read each set of sentences. In each set of sentences, there are two blanks. Circle the letter choice for the correct word that goes in each blank.

Bees, wasps, and yellow jackets notice what people wear. They are especially attracted to clothes with bright colors and floral (1) _____ . They are also (2) _____ toward people who wear perfume or hair spray. People who don't want to be stung will wear neutral-colored clothing and forget perfume and hair spray.

1. (A) notepaper   (B) wallpaper   (C) names   (D) patterns
2. (A) proposed   (B) labeled   (C) lured   (D) blushed

In China purple is the color of (3) _____ . An American manufacturer once packaged chewing gum in a purple wrapper. When he attempted to market it in China, he discovered sales were poor. The Chinese believed the gum could only be chewed at (4) _____ .

3. (A) life   (B) spring   (C) disease   (D) death
4. (A) games   (B) funerals   (C) dances   (D) parades

If you were told that suits weigh less today than they did thirty years ago, would you believe it? It is a fact. Men's suits, for example, weighed five pounds in 1930. Men's suits today weigh less than two pounds. (5) _____ woolens are being replaced by (6) _____ materials.

5. (A) Smart   (B) Coarse   (C) Clever   (D) Heavy
6. (A) massive   (B) drab   (C) lighter   (D) weighty

Criminals prefer to work at night. Darkness gives them the protective covering they need, and their chances of being (7) _____ or caught are considerably lessened. Since other people are usually asleep or less alert, criminals can work at night without unnecessary (8) _____ .

7. (A) added   (B) identified   (C) awakened   (D) tired
8. (A) interference   (B) talking   (C) directions   (D) noise

Early pioneer homes often stood many miles apart, with nothing between but forests. A visitor was a rare treat, and pioneer families were happy to (9) _____ their (10) _____ to any stranger who happened along. A guest bearing news or a good tale was particularly welcome.

9. (A) offer   (B) divide   (C) question   (D) consider
10. (A) animals   (B) hospitality   (C) stories   (D) work

ANSWER KEY

FOLLOWING DIRECTIONS

NAME _____

Read each set of directions, then circle the letter choice that best answers the question about the directions.

DIRECTIONS: The only ingredients you will need are a cup of water and one and three quarters of a cup of granulated sugar. First boil the water. Then take it off the heat and stir in the sugar. For colored rock candy, add a drop or two of food coloring. Then let the solution cool. Next carefully heat a glass jar by running hot water over it, and pour in the sugar solution. Let the solution stand while you tie a string around a pencil that is longer than the mouth of the jar. Make sure that the length of the string is the same as the height of the jar. Then place the pencil across the top of the jar with the string hanging down into the solution. As the solution stands for several days, the sugar crystals will form around the string.

1. These directions show you how to—
   (A) make rock candy   (B) make a sugar syrup
   (C) freeze sugar   (D) purify sugar

2. Before stirring the sugar into the water,—
   (A) tie the string to the pencil   (B) boil the water
   (C) heat a glass jar well   (D) put the string into the water

3. After the sugar solution cools,—
   (A) pour it into a cool jar   (B) pour it into a heated jar
   (C) stand a pencil in it   (D) add food coloring

4. The sugar crystals will form—
   (A) around the pencil   (B) in a few days
   (C) almost immediately   (D) when you add more sugar

3

GETTING THE MAIN IDEA

NAME _____

Read the stories, then, on the opposite page, circle the letter choice for the sentence that tells the main idea of the story.

1. Compared with the fourteen-thousand-foot peaks of the Rockies, Mt. Washington in New Hampshire may seem relatively small at 6,288 feet high. However, the top of Mt. Washington has unbelievably treacherous weather. In moments the weather can change from a sunny to a stormy day—often with fierce gales. No wonder the building on this mountaintop is chained to the ground!

2. Many fighters for women's equality say it's about time the United States put a woman's portrait on some of its paper money. Few people know, however, that two women have already achieved that honor, a century ago. Martha Washington's face graced a one-dollar bill and Pocahontas' picture appeared on a twenty-dollar bank note.

3. Trees use and give off a surprising amount of water. The water is taken in by the roots and released by the leaves. It has been estimated that eighty gallons of water a day may evaporate from the average tree. A white oak tree will give off 150 gallons of moisture in a single day during hot weather. A large oak tree will give off 28,000 gallons of water during one growing season!

4. The North Pole is not the world's coldest region. Northeastern Siberia, over one thousand miles south of the North Pole, is the coldest place on earth. Temperatures as low as eighty degrees below zero Fahrenheit (−62.2 Celsius) have often been recorded. Oddly enough, you would seldom catch a cold in the world's coldest region. Most germs cannot live in such extreme cold!

5. The mystery of how salmon can find their way back to their home rivers is solved. A salmon navigates by sun and stars when traveling in the ocean. When the salmon nears the general area of the river in which it was born, it uses its nose. The salmon can remember the smell of the home river that it left as a baby.

4

GETTING THE MAIN IDEA

NAME _____

1. The paragraph tells mainly—
   (A) why people climb to the top of Mt. Washington
   (B) why Mt. Washington is smaller than the Rockies
   (C) why the weather can change so fast at the top of Mt. Washington
   (D) why the top of Mt. Washington is treacherous

2. The paragraph tells mainly—
   (A) why women should be pictured on paper money
   (B) when women's portraits were printed on paper money
   (C) how people fight for equality
   (D) why women are no longer pictured on paper money

3. The paragraph tells mainly—
   (A) how much water trees give off
   (B) how trees give off water
   (C) what trees give off the least water
   (D) how trees take in water

4. The paragraph tells mainly—
   (A) how cold it gets
   (B) why people don't catch cold
   (C) what the coldest region is like
   (D) what the North Pole is like

5. The paragraph tells mainly—
   (A) what a mystery is
   (B) how far salmon travel
   (C) what salmon remember
   (D) how salmon find their way home

5

DRAWING CONCLUSIONS

NAME _____

Read the short stories, then, on the opposite page, circle the letter choice that describes something you can tell from the information in the story. Use clues in each story to draw a conclusion to find the correct answer.

1. English women once thought they looked best with wigs that rose two or even three feet above their heads. They certainly looked taller. Wool, cotton, and goats' hair were used to give the hairpieces the desired height. The finest high-piled wigs were often decorated with imitation fruit, model ships, horses, and figurines.

2. Though Americans take pride in the accomplishments of the pony express, few people know of an earlier and equally remarkable postal service. Eight hundred years before the pony express operated, messages traveled 150 miles a day—without the aid of a horse! Inca Indian runners were spaced about three miles apart over a stone road that stretched five thousand miles. These relay runners were the "express mail" carriers of their time.

3. When a large number of soldiers march across a small bridge, they are usually told to break step. If the bridge isn't particularly strong and the soldiers march in step, they can start a vibration that can cause the bridge to collapse. That is also the main reason why trains go slowly across bridges. A faster motion could set up vibrations and increase the danger of a bridge disaster.

4. The liver is the largest of the body's glands. It helps the body absorb food by producing a fluid that breaks down the food taken into the body. The liver keeps a close watch on the bloodstream, clearing the blood of many harmful products it can absorb. The liver also stores sugar for future use and makes sure that the heart does not become overloaded with blood.

5. By actually fishing for and catching other fish, the angler fish grows to be almost four feet long. It lies quietly in mud at the bottom of the water. Three wormlike "fingers" on the top of its head attract other fish. When the fish come close, the angler fish gets its meal. If fishing is slow, the angler fish may rise to the surface and swallow ducks, loons, or even geese.

6

DRAWING CONCLUSIONS

NAME _____

1. From the story you cannot tell—
   (A) how wigs were decorated
   (B) how high the wigs were
   (C) what the wigs were made of
   (D) the color of the wigs

2. The best nickname for these Indian messengers would be—
   (A) Pony Express
   (B) Inca Express
   (C) Eight-hundred-year Mail
   (D) Horseless Carriage

3. Trains go slowly across bridges—
   (A) because bridges are long
   (B) because trains are long
   (C) for more than one reason
   (D) because most bridges are weak

4. The liver performs—
   (A) one function
   (B) two functions
   (C) four functions
   (D) three functions

5. You can conclude that angler fish—
   (A) prefer fish to other animals
   (B) have worms growing out of their heads
   (C) are often eaten by birds
   (D) always remain at the bottom of the water

7

IDENTIFYING INFERENCES

NAME _____

Read the short stories. On the opposite page, read the sentences about each story. Decide whether each sentence is true (T), false (F), or an inference (I). A true sentence tells a fact from the story. A false sentence tells something that is not true. An inference says something that is *probably* true, based on facts in the story. More than one sentence about each story may be true, false, or an inference. Place an X in the correct box to mark your answer.

1. Mr. Gomes noticed a fresh, slick stain on the floor of his garage, right where the front of his car usually stops. "Oh, oh," he thought. "Something's leaking from my car." He bent down and sniffed the stain. "Doesn't smell like oil." He checked the water in the radiator and the brake fluid. "Both full. No leaks there. I don't have power steering or air conditioning, and my windshield-washer-fluid container has been empty for months. There are no other possibilities. It's a mystery."

2. "Who hid my hat?" asked Ralph angrily. "I know one of you did."
   "Why would anyone want to hide your hat?" inquired Tanya.
   Ralph scowled. "I know you all dislike me, and I don't care. Everyone's been against me from the moment I arrived here from my other school," said Ralph to his classmates. "Well, you won't have to put up with me anymore. I'm leaving!" Ralph grabbed his coat off the rack. When he did, his hat fell out from underneath. Ralph had hidden his hat from himself.

3. "We're out of eggs, Sis," Willis complained. "We can't make the supper."
   "I was afraid we might be," declared Sis. "In this cold weather, Mom usually stops at the Hope Diner on her way home from work for a cup of hot tea. The waiter knows her. Let's call the diner and leave a message for her." Sis dialed the diner.
   An hour later Mom came in with a bag of groceries, but no eggs.

4. "You said there was a river near here. Why don't we go swimming?" suggested Tina.
   "Oh, you wouldn't want to swim in that river!" said Karen.
   "Why not?" Tina asked. "I'm a strong swimmer. Even if the river's deep or the current's fast, it won't bother me."
   "It's not that the river is fast or deep," said Karen. "If you like swimming with tires, bottles and rusty cans, you can swim there."
   "Well," said Tina, "I don't particularly want to swim in a polluted river. Let's think of something better to do."

5. Kim was delighted to visit her cousin in Mexico, but she hadn't expected such hot weather. "I really can't stand this heat," she confided to her cousin.
   "Tomorrow will be better," her cousin assured her. "I've arranged for us to swim in our neighbor's outdoor pool."
   "Oh boy!" shouted Kim. "A plunge into cold, refreshing water. I can't wait!"
   "Er, uh," sighed her cousin, "don't get your hopes up too high."

8

65

ANSWER KEY

NAME _____

IDENTIFYING INFERENCES

T F I

1. (A) Mr. Gomes considered six possibilities for the leak.
   (B) Mr. Gomes will ask a mechanic to solve the mystery.
   (C) The liquid stain smelled like oil.
   (D) Mr. Gomes solved the mystery.

2. (A) Tanya was sitting on Ralph's hat.
   (B) Ralph had previously attended another school.
   (C) Ralph expected people to pick on him.
   (D) Ralph's hat was under his coat.

3. (A) Mom had gone shopping instead of stopping at the diner for tea.
   (B) Willis discovered that there were no eggs in the house.
   (C) Mom had a dozen eggs in her bag of groceries.
   (D) Sis decided to call the diner and leave a message.

4. (A) The weather was warm enough for outdoor swimming.
   (B) No other outdoor pools or bodies of water were located nearby.
   (C) Tina was afraid to swim in a river with a fast current.
   (D) Karen told Tina about the trash in the river.

5. (A) The pool water could not be cooled in any way.
   (B) The neighbors had an indoor pool.
   (C) Kim had not expected Mexico to be so hot.
   (D) Kim did not enjoy visiting her cousin.

9

NAME _____

GETTING THE FACTS

Read the story, then, on the opposite page, circle the letter choice that best completes each sentence about the story.

Pioneer Woman of the Sky

Lightning ripped through the blackness over the mid-Atlantic Ocean. The small plane's engine sputtered. The slim young woman at the controls knew she was too far out to turn back. Carefully she coaxed the plane ahead through the storm.

When dawn came, the engine was failing seriously. Just ahead lay the Irish coast. As the engine gasped its last, the woman brought her plane down in a cow pasture. An astonished farmer raced over as the young woman climbed out of the airplane. "I'm from America," she said. "My name is Amelia Earhart." She had become the first woman ever to fly the Atlantic alone. She had even set a new speed record, thirteen hours and thirty minutes!

Many people had told Amelia Earhart not to make this flight. They didn't think a woman was strong enough to keep going through the long night. However, Earhart had strength and courage to spare. She had already made parachute jumps and had explored the ocean floor in a diver's suit. Now, overnight, she had become famous.

She then began to dream of circling the globe at its widest part. Money was raised, and Earhart bought a new plane. In her first attempt, however, her plane was damaged on takeoff and she had to delay the flight. By the time the plane was repaired, the season had changed.

The world anxiously followed her flight. She flew across central Africa, Arabia, and the Orient. Finally, only one difficult stop remained. She would have to find a tiny speck in the Pacific—Howland Island.

As the world waited, a message crackled from her radio. People could not believe it. The message said, "Circling . . . cannot see island . . . gas is running low." For two weeks, warships and planes searched the ocean for the daring young woman and her copilot, Fred Noonan. No trace was ever found.

Today many airplanes, both commercial and military, follow the path blazed in the sky by the fearless woman aviator—Amelia Earhart.

10

NAME _____

GETTING THE FACTS

1. The woman at the controls was flying—
   (A) a kite
   (B) a jumbo jet
   (C) through a storm
   (D) with two copilots

2. She brought the airplane down—
   (A) on a beach
   (B) in a cow pasture
   (C) in a deserted village
   (D) in Boston

3. Amelia Earhart was the first woman to—
   (A) fly the Atlantic alone
   (B) cross America
   (C) fly solo
   (D) fly to Miami

4. Amelia made her trip in a little over—
   (A) thirteen hours
   (B) twenty hours
   (C) six hours
   (D) fifty hours

5. Amelia had also explored—
   (A) the Klondike region
   (B) Africa
   (C) the jungle
   (D) the ocean floor

6. She planned to—
   (A) reach the South Pole
   (B) circle the globe
   (C) reach China
   (D) reach the Arctic

7. On takeoff her airplane—
   (A) caught fire
   (B) was damaged
   (C) crashed
   (D) rose sharply

8. Amelia Earhart intended to land—
   (A) in Japan
   (B) on Howland Island
   (C) in the Marshalls
   (D) in Panama

9. A message from Amelia said that—
   (A) her copilot was ill
   (B) her time was up
   (C) all was well
   (D) the gas was low

10. Amelia and her plane—
    (A) disappeared
    (B) circled the globe
    (C) reached Honolulu
    (D) landed safely

11

NAME _____

DETECTING THE SEQUENCE

Read the story. As you read it, look for clues that let you know the order in which things happened. Then, on the opposite page, circle the letter choice that best answers the question about the sequence of events.

Elizabeth Blackwell, M.D.

In the early autumn of 1847, the professors of Geneva Medical College in New York held a meeting. Among the matters they discussed was a letter from Dr. William Elder of Philadelphia recommending that they admit Elizabeth Blackwell to the school. The professors were shocked. No American woman had ever been to an American medical school before. The idea of a woman doctor was ridiculous! They chose to pass the decision along to the students. Surely the young men would vote against Miss Blackwell. To the professors' surprise, they were wrong.

Elizabeth Blackwell received a letter from Geneva Medical College in late October telling her she could enter the school. Many months before, Blackwell had applied to thirty medical schools, but Geneva was the only one to admit her. On November 6, 1847, she attended her first lecture at Geneva Medical College. Two years later, she graduated at the top of her class.

Now Dr. Blackwell wanted to become a surgeon, and she traveled to Paris to continue her studies. None of the teaching hospitals there would accept a woman doctor, however, so she entered Paris' largest women's hospital as a nursing student instead. Four months after she began working there, Dr. Blackwell caught an eye infection from a patient. She lost her sight in one eye, thus ruining her chances to become a surgeon.

In 1851, Dr. Blackwell settled in New York City. She set up a doctor's office, but her landlord refused to let her hang up a sign. No patients came for months. Meanwhile, she presented a series of lectures on "the physical education of girls." Stacy Collins, one of the women in the audience, was so impressed with Dr. Blackwell that she became the doctor's first patient.

By 1854, Dr. Blackwell was able to make a living as a doctor. Three years later, she opened a hospital, the New York Infirmary for Women and Children. During its first year, the hospital treated three hundred patients. The next year, however, it treated three thousand. Still, Dr. Blackwell had even higher hopes. She urged New York to start a women's medical college. Finally, in 1866, the New York Women's Medical College held its first class. Among the professors teaching there was Elizabeth Blackwell, M.D.

12

NAME _____

DETECTING THE SEQUENCE

1. Which of these events happened first?
   (A) Elizabeth Blackwell traveled to Paris to study.
   (B) Elizabeth Blackwell applied to thirty medical schools.
   (C) Elizabeth Blackwell attended her first lecture at Geneva Medical College.
   (D) Students at Geneva voted whether to admit Elizabeth Blackwell.

2. Which of these events happened last?
   (A) Elizabeth Blackwell settled in New York City.
   (B) Stacy Collins became Dr. Blackwell's first patient.
   (C) Dr. Blackwell taught at the New York Women's Medical College.
   (D) The New York Infirmary for Women and Children treated 300 patients.

3. What happened soon after Dr. Blackwell began working at Paris' largest women's hospital?
   (A) The hospital treated three thousand patients.
   (B) She caught an eye infection from a patient.
   (C) Geneva Medical College admitted her.
   (D) She presented a series of lectures.

4. Which occurred after Dr. Blackwell presented lectures on "the physical education of girls"?
   (A) Stacy Collins became Dr. Blackwell's first patient.
   (B) Geneva Medical College admitted Elizabeth Blackwell.
   (C) Dr. Blackwell set up a doctor's office in New York.
   (D) Dr. Blackwell traveled to Paris to continue her studies.

5. When did Dr. Blackwell open the New York Infirmary for Women and Children?
   (A) while she attended Geneva Medical College
   (B) after she taught at the New York Women's Medical College
   (C) before she studied nursing in Paris
   (D) after she set up a doctor's office in New York

13

NAME _____

FOLLOWING DIRECTIONS

Read each set of directions, then circle the letter choice that best answers the question about the directions.

DIRECTIONS: The TV weather report announces a tornado warning! It tells you to take shelter. Turn off all electrical devices. If you have a battery-powered radio, keep it with you. If you live in a mobile home, go to a community storm shelter. In a house or apartment, do not open windows. Open windows do not prevent severe wind damage. Go to a basement and get under a table or workbench. If you have no basement, go to an inner area far from windows, such as a hallway, inner bedroom, or closet. Crouch under a mattress or other thick bedding. Stay sheltered until the storm is over.

1. This paragraph was written to tell you how to—
   (A) take shelter during a storm
   (B) turn off the electricity
   (C) draw a plan of your home
   (D) choose a battery radio

2. Opening windows is not helpful because—
   (A) you will get cold
   (B) rain will soak the floor
   (C) it wastes time
   (D) wind damage still occurs

3. Getting under a workbench or table protects you from—
   (A) rain
   (B) lightning
   (C) cold
   (D) flying or falling material

4. Halls, inner bedrooms, or closets are safest because—
   (A) they are stronger
   (B) they are away from the wind
   (C) they have a workbench
   (D) they have been painted recently

14

66

ANSWER KEY

NAME

USING THE CONTEXT

Read each set of sentences. In each set of sentences, there are two blanks. Circle the letter choice for the correct word that goes in each blank.

It's now possible to fly fairly close to a hospital in the thick jungle of Africa. The hospital, near Lambarene, was (1) _____ by Dr. Schweitzer in 1913. Each of the (2) _____ who visit Schweitzer Hospital annually is asked to donate a pint of blood.

1. (A) computed   (B) alphabetized   (C) established   (D) barbecued
2. (A) skeletons   (B) pigeons   (C) submarines   (D) tourists

People sometimes capture birds and place metal bands around their legs. Then the birds are released. When the banded birds are caught again, the metal tags tell where the birds have come from. Bird banding helps scientists (3) _____ more (4) _____ about the travel habits of birds.

3. (A) send   (B) overlook   (C) gain   (D) grow
4. (A) messengers   (B) trips   (C) caution   (D) information

Instead of producing a timid squeal, the grasshopper mouse makes a sound like a wolf. Its (5) _____ can be heard 100 yards away. This fearless mouse not only eats grasshoppers but also attacks creatures three times its size. Yet it (6) _____ other mice in appearance.

5. (A) purr   (B) neigh   (C) baa   (D) howl
6. (A) outlaws   (B) weaves   (C) smells   (D) resembles

Southeast of Japan is a stretch of water that the Japanese know as the Devil's Sea. Between 1950 and 1954 nine large freighters (7) _____ in this area without a (8) _____. A vessel sent out to search the area vanished also, complete with crew and scientists!

7. (A) reappeared   (B) vanished   (C) collided   (D) assembled
8. (A) warning   (B) sound   (C) trace   (D) signal

Blood circulates through the body in blood vessels. There are more of these than you might (9) _____. If they were (10) _____ in a row, the vessels would stretch for 100,000 miles, enough to circle the earth four times.

9. (A) imagine   (B) doubt   (C) sing   (D) wonder
10. (A) piled   (B) laid   (C) buried   (D) hidden

15

NAME

GETTING THE MAIN IDEA

Read the stories, then, on the opposite page, circle the letter choice for the sentence that tells the main idea of the story.

1. The practice of wearing rings is a very ancient one. Over time, people in many lands have decorated their bodies by wearing rings on their fingers, ears, lips, necks, noses, ankles, and wrists. Some even wore rings on their toes. In some cultures, a married woman wore a ring on the big toe of her left foot; a man might put rings on his second and third toes as well.

2. The frankfurter, named for the city of Frankfurt in Germany, is easily the most popular sausage in the world. Frankfurters, popularly known as "hot dogs," are sold almost everywhere in the United States. They are consumed in great numbers at sporting events and amusement places. People from foreign countries often think hot dogs are one of the characteristics of American life.

3. Many ancient coins are not as valuable as people tend to think they are. In the early days the threat of a foreign invasion was common. People buried the family wealth, hoping to uncover it later when the threat was past. In many cases these people were killed or taken away as prisoners. Their coins are continually being uncovered by chance today and can be purchased for a modest price.

4. The Trans-Canadian Highway is the first ocean-to-ocean highway in Canada and the longest paved road in the world. After twelve years of work, the 4,859-mile highway was completed in September of 1962. The Trans-Canadian Highway makes it possible, for the first time, for a person to drive from coast to coast and remain within Canada for the entire trip.

5. The experts are not always right. They advised the big mining companies to pass up the Cripple Creek region. They claimed that there was no gold there. It was left up to local prospectors to uncover the incredible wealth of Cripple Creek. More than $400 million worth of ore was found in this area that experts ignored.

16

NAME

GETTING THE MAIN IDEA

1. The paragraph tells mainly—
   - (A) why some people wore rings on their toes
   - (B) what kinds of rings were the most popular
   - (C) when the practice of wearing rings first began
   - (D) how people in many lands have worn rings

2. The paragraph tells mainly—
   - (A) why hot dogs are popular
   - (B) how popular hot dogs are
   - (C) what foreign people think of hot dogs
   - (D) how hot dogs and frankfurters differ

3. The paragraph tells mainly—
   - (A) what happened during invasions
   - (B) why there are so few ancient coins today
   - (C) why many ancient coins are inexpensive
   - (D) why people were taken prisoners

4. The paragraph tells mainly—
   - (A) what the Trans-Canadian Highway is like
   - (B) how the Trans-Canadian Highway helps
   - (C) why the Trans-Canadian Highway was built
   - (D) where the longest road is

5. The paragraph tells mainly—
   - (A) what experts thought about Cripple Creek
   - (B) when the Cripple Creek gold was found
   - (C) how much the ore was worth
   - (D) how big mining companies operated

17

NAME

PROGRESS CHECK

Exploring Language

What makes a joke funny? To understand the humor of a joke, you need to draw conclusions about it. Read each of the following jokes. Answer the questions about the jokes.

Answers will vary.

1. Jan asked her teacher, "Would you scold someone for something she didn't do?" "Of course not," her teacher answered. "Why do you ask?" "Because I didn't do my math homework," Jan answered.

   What did the teacher mean when she said that she wouldn't scold someone for something she didn't do?

2. A traveler asked the ticket agent at a railroad station for a round trip ticket. "Where to?" the ticket agent asked. "Back to here," the traveler said.

   What did the ticket agent want to know?

3. Willy asked Billy, "Were you born in New York?" "Yes," Billy answered. "What part?" asked Willy. "All of me," said Billy.

   What did Willy want to know?

18

NAME

PROGRESS CHECK

Exercising Your Skill

An **analogy** is a way of comparing things. When we make an analogy, we are saying that things that are otherwise unlike *are* similar in some way. We are pointing out a relationship between two sets of things. For example:

Pitcher is to baseball as quarterback is to football.

In other words, a pitcher is one of the players in a baseball game, just as a quarterback is one of the players in a football game.

Analogies may show many different kinds of relationships. They may relate words with similar meanings (synonyms), words with opposite meanings (antonyms), parts to the whole, users to things used, or actions to objects.

Read each item below and draw a conclusion about the relationship between the sets of things. Ask yourself whether there is a relationship between the two sets of things. For each analogy, write *sense* or *no sense* to tell whether you think the analogy makes sense.

1. The **moon** is to the **earth** as the **earth** is to the **sun**.
   sense
2. **Puzzle** is to **solution** as **lock** is to **key**.
   sense
3. **Needles** are to **pine tree** as **leaves** are to **autumn**.
   no sense
4. **Reality** is to **fantasy** as **pleasure** is to **enjoyment**.
   no sense
5. **Gray** is to **black** as **pink** is to **red**.
   sense
6. **Ship** is to **port** as **car** is to **garage**.
   sense
7. **Row** is to **boat** as **pedal** is to **bicycle**.
   sense
8. **Fox** is to **den** as **grizzly** is to **bear**.
   no sense
9. **Pod** is to **pea** as **shell** is to **walnut**.
   sense
10. **Scissors** are to **sharp** as **stapler** is to **staple**.
    no sense

19

NAME

IDENTIFYING INFERENCES

Read the short stories. On the opposite page, read the sentences about each story. Decide whether each sentence is true (T), false (F), or an inference (I). A true sentence tells a fact from the story. A false sentence tells something that is not true. An inference says something that is *probably* true, based on facts in the story. More than one sentence about each story may be true, false, or an inference. Place an X in the correct box to mark your answer.

1. Lois waited for her turn to read her poem in front of the class. "This is a pretty good poem," she thought to herself. "It's just that. . . ." Then her name was called, she stood up, and her knees began to shake. When she turned around and looked at the rest of the class, however, she saw friendly faces. "Maybe this won't be so bad after all," Lois thought with relief.

2. Tommy was happily skipping homeward, whacking trees and lightpoles with a thin stick as he went—just for fun. Suddenly, as he struck a pole, all the lights in town went out. Tommy groped his way home. His parents were listening to a battery-powered radio in the dark. He slunk past them and hid under his bed. "So the power failure is statewide," said Tommy's mother to his father. "The reporter said that it was definitely caused by a faulty generator miles upstate."

3. The young man lay at the bottom of the cliff in a crumpled heap. The two girls who approached him thought he was dead, until. . . .
   "Please get help," he moaned in pain. "Call an ambulance." Dawn stayed with the man, while Grace ran to a nearby telephone.
   "What can I do to make you more comfortable?" asked Dawn.
   "Could you get these hoops of rope off my leg?" he requested.
   Soon the ambulance arrived. The paramedics said the man had some broken ribs but that he would be all right.

4. "Look at our new puppy—isn't he cute? We've named him Snowball," Craig said. "He needs to have puppy shots, though, and we don't know which doctor to take him to. Can you recommend a good vet?"
   "Of course," his neighbor answered. "We always go to Dr. Sylvia Miller. She was just terrific when Patches was so sick last summer. She identified the problem right away, and Patches was healthy and purring again within just a few days."

5. "The sun beamed down on the sweltering city streets. Carl and Evan moped along, sweating. "We've got to beat this heat," groaned Carl.
   "Let's take the subway to the beach," suggested Evan.
   "Neither one of us has enough money for the bus," said Carl. "We can't afford an air-conditioned movie, either."
   "I know," cried Evan. "Let's go to Benny's."
   "Great idea!" responded Carl, and they ran off.

20

67

ANSWER KEY

NAME _____

IDENTIFYING INFERENCES

		T	F	I
1.	(A) Lois went to the back of the room.			
	(B) Lois was afraid of speaking in front of the class.			
	(C) As soon as Lois stood up, she felt calm.			
	(D) The faces of her classmates were friendly.			

2.	(A) Tommy thought he had caused the power failure.			
	(B) When Tommy arrived home, his parents were watching TV.			
	(C) The cause of the power failure was far from Tommy's home.			
	(D) The power failed because Tommy struck the pole.			

3.	(A) The girls found the young man at the bottom of the cliff.			
	(B) The man asked the girls to call an ambulance.			
	(C) The man had been mountain climbing.			
	(D) At first the two girls thought the man was dead.			

4.	(A) Craig asked his neighbor to recommend a good vet.			
	(B) Patches is the neighbor's pet cat.			
	(C) The name of Craig's new puppy is Snowball.			
	(D) Patches died last summer.			

5.	(A) Carl suggested going to the beach.			
	(B) Benny's is a cool place.			
	(C) The boys could not afford the subway or the movies.			
	(D) Benny's is a place that costs little or no money.			

21

NAME _____

PROGRESS CHECK

Exploring Language

Choose one of these activities.

1. Here are several sentences about hurricanes. Look for the main idea sentence and its supporting sentences. Then rearrange the supporting sentences into a clear paragraph. Do not include the two sentences that do not support the main idea sentence. Finally, give the paragraph a title.

* The eye of a hurricane is usually about 14 miles across.
* Winds stretch out from the eye several hundred miles in all directions.
* The shape of a hurricane is unique.
* The word "hurricane" comes from a West Indian word, *huracan*, which means "evil spirit."
* It is the only storm that has a calm center, or "eye."
* Winds and rains around the eye are the strongest.
* The hurricane season in the Northern Hemisphere lasts from June through November.
* However, an eye twice the normal size is not unusual.
* Air around the eye swirls upward like smoke in a chimney.

Answers will vary.

_____

_____

_____

_____

Write your title for the paragraph.

2. Write four or five sentences on another piece of paper in support of the following main idea.

The real damage from a hurricane occurs when the storm strikes an area where a lot of people live.

22

NAME _____

USING THE CONTEXT

Read each set of sentences. In each set of sentences, there are two blanks. Circle the letter choice for the correct word that goes in each blank.

When people apply perfume or after-shave lotion to their faces or behind their ears, only those friends and associates about a foot and a half taller than the users can (1) _____ the aroma well. Since odors rise, people should put pleasing scents on their (2) _____ or knees.

1. (A) honor   (B) detect   (C) unwrap   (D) dissolve
2. (A) foreheads   (B) hair   (C) ankles   (D) eyebrows

When the telephone first came into use, people considered it impolite to phone someone at home without being (3) _____ to do so. The first phone book was printed in 1870. It contained only 271 (4) _____, none of which were personal. Only companies were listed.

3. (A) petitioned   (B) licensed   (C) qualified   (D) invited
4. (A) subjects   (B) listings   (C) categories   (D) classifications

Jules Verne, one of the first writers of science fiction, foresaw television a hundred years ago. He called it "phonotelephoto." He also foresaw the skyscrapers of today. Most remarkably, he (5) _____ the first trip to the (6) _____ from a launching spot near the one actually used!

5. (A) made   (B) predicted   (C) arranged   (D) recorded
6. (A) moon   (B) sun   (C) universe   (D) crater

(7) _____ in ancient Rome were highly (8) _____. If the script called for a fire, the stage would be put to the torch. If an attack by a wild animal was indicated, an actor would engage in a fight to the death with a real live bear!

7. (A) Games   (B) Plays   (C) Contests   (D) Exhibits
8. (A) appealing   (B) artistic   (C) symbolic   (D) realistic

Would you be surprised if you saw a baby larger than its parents? This happens with birds. The parents stuff the baby with food. Within a few weeks the baby is often larger than either parent. When it flies off to (9) _____ for its own food, it (10) _____ weight.

9. (A) purchase   (B) gather   (C) raise   (D) search
10. (A) obtains   (B) remains   (C) loses   (D) gains

23

NAME _____

GETTING THE FACTS

Read the story, then, on the opposite page, circle the letter choice that best completes each sentence about the story.

Ghost Ship of World War II

"I don't believe it," said the sailor on board the United States Navy destroyer. It was during World War II, and the sailor was looking at an enemy ship. "That destroyer flies the Japanese flag," the sailor shouted, "but it looks like an American ship!" Then the guns of the strange warship opened fire, and once again the air over the Pacific Ocean rocked to the sounds of battle.

It was not the first time this dangerous warship had fired at the American navy. But no American sailor could ever figure out its name. It was not on any chart. It did not match any pictures of Japanese destroyers in navy files. Yet it looked like many other American ships. Soon American sailors were calling this mysterious craft the Ghost Ship of World War II.

The story of the Ghost Ship is a very strange one. On February 26, 1942, the American destroyer *Stewart* was damaged by the Japanese. It was ordered back to port for repairs. But Japanese airplanes attacked it again and scored a direct hit. American officers then ordered a retreat. The crew abandoned ship, and the *Stewart* was left behind.

Three weeks later the *Stewart* was taken off the list of U.S. Navy ships. But no one knew that the Japanese had captured the American warship and rebuilt it. Soon it was fighting side by side with Japanese destroyers. Time and time again, the Ghost Ship saw action against the American navy. Throughout the entire war, no American was able to solve the mystery.

But the end of the tale is even stranger. After the Americans won the war, they found an old rusty destroyer in a Japanese port. It had been abandoned by the Japanese. The Americans checked their records and lists of ships. They were surprised to find that the Japanese destroyer was really the old USS *Stewart*. The mystery of the Ghost Ship of World War II was finally solved.

24

NAME _____

GETTING THE FACTS

1. The strange enemy warship flew the flag of—
   (A) Germany   (B) Italy
   (C) Japan   (D) the United States
2. Both ships were traveling in the—
   (A) Atlantic Ocean   (B) Indian Ocean
   (C) Black Sea   (D) Pacific Ocean
3. American sailors named this craft the Ghost Ship of—
   (A) World War III   (B) World War II
   (C) Japan   (D) World War I
4. The name of the destroyer that was damaged by the Japanese was the—
   (A) Stewart   (B) Seaworth
   (C) Saunders   (D) Stephen
5. The destroyer was left behind by the—
   (A) Japanese   (B) army
   (C) marines   (D) navy
6. Unknown to the navy, the ship was captured by the—
   (A) Army   (B) Japanese
   (C) Russians   (D) Germans
7. After the war, the destroyer was—
   (A) lost   (B) painted
   (C) found   (D) sold
8. This time the Ghost Ship was discarded by the—
   (A) Germans   (B) Chinese
   (C) United States   (D) Japanese
9. Surprisingly, the Ghost Ship was really the—
   (A) USS Stewart   (B) UAR Stewart
   (C) USS Stillman   (D) SSU Stewart
10. The Ghost Ship mystery was—
    (A) taped   (B) unknown
    (C) solved   (D) recorded

25

NAME _____

PROGRESS CHECK

Exercising Your Skill

There are different kinds of directions. Some directions are the kind you see in workbooks and on tests. Some directions tell you how to do or make something. Others tell you how to carry out an experiment.

Read these sets of directions. Think about what the directions tell you to do. Match each set of directions with a title from the box. In the space provided, write the title that fits the directions.

Experiment Directions	Game Directions
How-To Directions	Workbook Directions

1. Read about ducks. Decide how the kinds of ducks are the same or different. Then underline the answer to each question.

   Title ____Workbook Directions____

2. You can make bongo drums with two coffee cans—one large and one small—their lids, and some masking tape. Snap the lids onto the cans. Turn the cans upside down and stand them on a table. Have someone hold the cans while you wind tape around them to hold them together. Turn the cans right side up, and drum away with your hands.

   Title ____How-To Directions____

3. Which reflects the sun's rays better, black or white? Put two thermometers in the sun. Cover one with a white cloth and one with a black cloth. After half an hour, take off the cloth and check the temperature. Which thermometer shows a lower temperature?

   Title ____Experiment Directions____

4. You will need seven or eight people and several different objects. All the players sit in a circle and sing a song together. Pass the objects around. When the song is over, everyone who is caught with an object has to make up a skit about it. When the skits are finished, start again. Skits can't be repeated. If someone can't think of a new skit, he or she is out!

   Title ____Game Directions____

26

ANSWER KEY

ANSWER KEY

IDENTIFYING INFERENCES

		T	F	I
1.	(A) The customer examined the restaurant's tableware.			☒
	(B) The customer said she liked her fish baked.		☒	
	(C) Mel insisted that only broiled fish could be served.	☒		
	(D) The new owner was pleased with Mel's reply.			☒
2.	(A) The dog was suffering pain.			☒
	(B) Larry had never seen an x-ray machine before.			☒
	(C) Larry's dog, Sam, had been hit by a car.	☒		
	(D) Sam was wrapped in a blanket.		☒	
3.	(A) Howard Ross grows more tense the longer he sits.			☒
	(B) Janice observes her subject very carefully.	☒		
	(C) Janice uses pastel chalk for her work.		☒	
	(D) Janice will paint Howard's portrait.			☒
4.	(A) Wendy was working on a science report.			☒
	(B) Wendy was aware of the rule about missing practice.	☒		
	(C) Wendy decided to miss practice to finish the report.		☒	
	(D) Wendy heard the coach's wife answer the phone.			☒
5.	(A) Rachel kept her only spare house key hidden under the doormat.		☒	
	(B) When Rachel had left her keys at work, she found the house key under the rock.			☒
	(C) After Rachel's purse had been stolen, she found the house key under the rock.	☒		
	(D) Rachel had forgotten to replace her house key under the rock.			☒

33

DETECTING THE SEQUENCE

Read the story. As you read it, look for clues that let you know the order in which things happened. Then, on the opposite page, circle the letter choice that best answers the question about the sequence of events.

Adventurous Nellie Bly

Reading the *Pittsburgh Dispatch* one day, Elizabeth Cochrane was upset by an editorial. It seemed to say that women were not the equals of men. Cochrane fired off an angry reply. The *Dispatch*'s editors were so impressed by the teenager's writing that they offered her a job.

Elizabeth Cochrane soon became a star at the *Pittsburgh Dispatch*. Then she took on the pen name Nellie Bly and wrote many newspaper articles. Her stories about poor living conditions in Pittsburgh were widely read. Businesses who advertised in the *Dispatch* were unhappy with the articles, however. They asked the paper to send Bly on vacation. She went to Mexico and began writing about conditions there. Soon the Mexican government also asked her to leave.

Then Nellie Bly moved on to New York City. She joined the staff of the *New York World*, where she quickly made a name for herself. No adventure was too great for Bly. First, she posed as an immigrant worker to expose dishonest hiring agencies. Next, she arranged to get arrested on false theft charges. Then Bly wrote articles about the terrible conditions she found in prison. Once she jumped off a ferry to see how quickly its rescue crew responded.

In 1889, Bly set out on her greatest adventure. Sixteen years before, Jules Verne's novel *Around the World in Eighty Days* had been published. The book described an eighty-day balloon trip around the world. Bly said she could beat that imaginary record. She set out from New York on November 14, 1889. After crossing the Atlantic, Bly stopped in France. There she interviewed the book's author, Jules Verne. She went on to Egypt, India, China, and Japan, and then crossed the Pacific to San Francisco. Bly raced across the United States toward New Jersey, just across the river from New York. Meanwhile, readers of the *New York World* eagerly followed her journey.

Seventy-two days and six hours after she left, Bly arrived in Jersey City. Cannons boomed, whistles sounded, and crowds cheered. Nellie Bly waved happily, knowing she had beaten more than the clock. She had proved that women can do almost anything.

34

DETECTING THE SEQUENCE

1. **Which of these events happened first?**
   - (A) The *Pittsburgh Dispatch* hired Elizabeth Cochrane.
   - (B) Cochrane read an editorial in the *Pittsburgh Dispatch*.
   - (C) Cochrane wrote an angry letter to the *Dispatch*.
   - (D) Cochrane became a star at the *Pittsburgh Dispatch*.

2. **Which of these events happened last?**
   - (A) Bly arrived in Jersey City.
   - (B) Bly interviewed Jules Verne.
   - (C) Bly set out from New York.
   - (D) Bly crossed the Pacific to San Francisco.

3. **When did businesses that advertised in the *Dispatch* ask the paper to send Bly on vacation?**
   - (A) while she wrote articles about conditions in Mexico
   - (B) after she wrote about living conditions in Pittsburgh
   - (C) when the *Dispatch*'s editors offered her a job
   - (D) after she moved to New York City

4. **What did Nellie Bly do just after she moved to New York City?**
   - (A) She went to Mexico on vacation.
   - (B) She took the pen name Nellie Bly.
   - (C) She joined the staff of the *New York World*.
   - (D) She set off on a trip around the world.

5. **Which took place 16 years before Nellie Bly set out to circle the world?**
   - (A) *Around the World in Eighty Days* was published.
   - (B) Bly interviewed Jules Verne.
   - (C) *New York World* readers followed Bly's journey.
   - (D) Bly raced across the United States.

35

PROGRESS CHECK

Exploring Language

To supply the missing word in an analogy, draw a conclusion about the relationship between the words in the complete pair. Then supply a word that has the same relationship to the remaining word. Remember that the relationship between the words in each pair must be similar, and the items in each pair must be in the same order.

Read each of the following incomplete analogies. Write the word that correctly completes each analogy.   Answers will vary.

1. **Valuable** is to **precious** as **worthless** is to _____
2. **Poodle** is to _____ as **Siamese** is to **cat**.
3. _____ is to **firefighter** as **hammer** is to **carpenter**.
4. **Numbers** are to **mathematics** as _____ are to **language**.
5. **Above** is to _____ as **front** is to **back**.
6. **Strings** are to **guitar** as _____ are to **piano**.
7. **Flock** is to **geese** as _____ is to **horses**.
8. _____ is to **state** as **state** is to **country**.
9. **Fawn** is to **deer** as _____ is to **cow**.
10. **Rainbow trout** is to _____ as **eagle** is to **bird**.

Expressing Yourself

Choose one of these activities. Use another piece of paper for your responses.
Answers will vary.
1. Create your own analogies based on your favorite television or story characters, athletes, or entertainers from television, music, or movies. Share your analogies. Be sure you can explain the relationships within the analogies.
2. Write an analogy of your own based on each kind of relationship listed below. Look back at analogies at the top of the page for examples if you need help.
   1. antonyms
   2. item to category
   3. part to whole
   4. synonyms
   5. animal to its young

36

PROGRESS CHECK

Exploring Language

Let's see how good you are at drawing conclusions based on just three facts! Read each of the following items. Based on the overheard bits of conversation, tell what is happening.
Answers will vary.

1. "Get those ladders up there!" "Hoses on!" "There are people on the top floor!"

2. "It's almost time for the show to start." "Look at that line at the ticket booth!" "Do you want to get some popcorn?"

3. "The Flying Estradas will now perform their own version of the triple somersault!" "Drum roll, please!" "He's going to fall! Oh, I can't bear to watch!"

4. "Forty-second Street. This station is Forty-second Street." "Excuse me. Coming through." "Watch your step, please, and stay clear of the track."

5. "Please deposit 25 cents for the next three minutes." "Operator, I have no more change!" "This is a recording."

6. "Come, Sandy." "Exercise over. You can praise your dog now." "Good boy, Sandy!"

7. "Look! Bases loaded!" "How many outs?" "Maybe she'll hit a grand slam homer!"

8. "Open your test booklets and begin." "Answer all the questions." "No talking!"

37

FOLLOWING DIRECTIONS

Read each set of directions, then circle the letter choice that best answers the question about the directions.

DIRECTIONS: There are several things you can use for a container: a fishbowl, a candy jar, a big glass are good choices. The most suitable plants for your terrarium are small woodland growths, but any tropical flowers will do. After choosing your plants, plan the arrangement on a piece of paper. Next place coarse stone and charcoal in the bottom of your container. Add two inches of moist soil. Arrange your plants in the soil as you have planned. After the planting, use an atomizer to spray the soil with water. Cover the container with a small piece of glass. Place your completed terrarium where there is good light, but not in direct sunlight. This "plant world under glass" will spring to life before you know it.

1. These instructions will help you—
   - (A) tend a garden
   - (B) make paper flowers
   - (C) find tropical flowers
   - (D) build a terrarium

2. Before filling the terrarium, you should—
   - (A) use an atomizer
   - (B) plan the plant arrangement
   - (C) place it in good light
   - (D) cover the container

3. The moist soil should be added after—
   - (A) you use the atomizer
   - (B) the cover is removed
   - (C) the stone and charcoal
   - (D) the terrarium is covered

4. After spraying the soil, you should—
   - (A) add more dirt
   - (B) add the charcoal
   - (C) arrange the plants
   - (D) cover the container

38

70

ANSWER KEY

USING THE CONTEXT

NAME _____

Read each set of sentences. In each set of sentences, there are two blanks. Circle the letter choice for the correct word that goes in each blank.

Do you ever ask someone to "hang loose"? If you do, you want the person to be more calm, unworried, and (1) _____. This expression originated back in 1950. It is the (2) _____ of being hung up, which means being in a state of nervous tension.

1. **(A) relaxed** (B) irritated (C) ignorant (D) isolated
2. (A) identical **(B) opposite** (C) illustration (D) pursuit

Can loud noises harm your health? To find out, scientists subjected rats to loud and frequent noise. Examinations showed that they acted very much like humans undergoing a (3) _____ (4) _____. They developed ulcers, lost their appetites, and found it difficult to make decisions.

3. (A) contagious (B) healthy **(C) nervous** (D) medical
4. (A) examination (B) buildup **(C) breakdown** (D) operation

After the *Titanic* was sent to the bottom of the sea by an iceberg in 1912, the Ice Patrol was founded. The patrol charts the (5) _____ of bergs in the North Atlantic. While the patrol has been active, not a single (6) _____ has been lost because of icebergs.

5. (A) size (B) history **(C) movements** (D) temperature
6. (A) record (B) day **(C) raft** (D) life

The chalk used to write on the board at school is actually gypsum. Chalk would (7) _____ too easily to be effective. Real chalk is used in (8) _____ that scour and polish. It is also widely used in a cleansing agent known to all of us—toothpaste.

7. (A) harden **(B) burn** (C) crumble (D) meet
8. (A) gargles **(B) powders** (C) acids (D) bleaches

It is a common belief that a very cold winter follows an unusually hot summer. Weather experts say there is no evidence for this belief. If a summer has been hotter than usual, the winter that follows seems (9) _____ than (10) _____.

9. (A) wetter (B) longer **(C) colder** (D) milder
10. (A) winter **(B) usual** (C) spring (D) frost

39

GETTING THE MAIN IDEA

NAME _____

Read the stories, then, on the opposite page, circle the letter choice for the sentence that tells the main idea of the story.

1. What do you think is the most popular soda flavor in the United States? If you thought of cola, you are right. Almost two out of every three cans or bottles of soda that are sold are cola. The second most popular flavor is lemon-lime, but that is far behind cola. Orange, ginger ale, grape, and root beer are next down the list.

2. Electric companies may put a special "clock" in everyone's kitchen soon. Numbers flash on the screen of this "clock," telling how much electricity is being used in the home at the moment and how much the monthly electric bill is to that moment. Electric companies think people will use less electricity if they realize how much it is costing them.

3. Art in its many forms has built a bridge between our civilization and the cultures that preceded it. Pictures on pottery have revealed many aspects of the life and times of people of particular eras. The painter has pictured civilizations that once flourished and died. Music and dancing also reflect the characters and emotions of our ancestors.

4. Among those who guard the city of Philadelphia are thirty-five chickens. The birds are kept by Philadelphia's Health Department to help assure that no deadly disease strikes the city. Each summer the birds are allowed to be bitten by mosquitoes that fly around the city. The medical workers test the chickens' blood. If the blood contains no disease germs, doctors know the mosquitoes are harmless.

5. A buffalo stampede was a frightening thing to see. The shaggy-headed buffalo, each weighing from one to two thousand pounds, rushed forward, heads low, smashing, trampling, and destroying everything in their way. Their sharp hoofs kicked up dust as they rushed blindly forward, bringing death and destruction to anyone and anything unlucky enough to be caught in their path.

40

GETTING THE MAIN IDEA

NAME _____

1. The paragraph tells mainly—
   (A) how far behind cola lemon-lime is
   (B) why Americans prefer cola
   (C) what soda flavors Americans prefer
   (D) which nation drinks the most soda

2. The paragraph tells mainly—
   (A) when the special "clock" will operate
   (B) where the special "clock" will be
   (C) whom the special "clock" will be for
   (D) what the special "clock" will do

3. The paragraph tells mainly—
   (A) why artists like history
   (B) how music and dancing reveal the past
   (C) how people learn about themselves
   (D) how various art forms help people learn history

4. The paragraph tells mainly—
   (A) how birds protect a city
   (B) how mosquitoes infect birds
   (C) how mosquitoes carry diseases
   (D) how the Health Department thought of using chickens

5. The paragraph tells mainly—
   (A) how heavy buffalo are
   (B) what a buffalo stampede was like
   (C) how hard buffalo charge
   (D) why people are afraid of some animals

41

DRAWING CONCLUSIONS

NAME _____

Read the short stories, then, on the opposite page, circle the letter choice that describes something you can tell from the information in the story. Use clues in each story to draw a conclusion to find the correct answer.

1. Ships that carry freight but do not travel on regular runs are called "tramps." A tramp steamer has no fixed schedule. It wanders from port to port. Declining in numbers in recent years, tramp steamers are less and less often seen. When the last of the tramp steamers has made its final port call, a little of the romance of the old sailing days will have vanished.

2. The rhinoceros is regarded by hunters as one of the most dangerous animals in the world. Despite its size, the animal gallops along at twenty-five to thirty-five miles an hour. Its horn gives it a formidable weapon. What is worse, the rhino has a mean temper. Without any apparent reason, the tanklike creature will attack even a railroad train!

3. Elephants display surprising intelligence. In the London Zoo elephants were separated from the public by two fences. Sometimes peanuts thrown by the onlookers landed between these fences, beyond the reach of both the people and the elephants. With a blast of air from their trunks, the elephants simply blew the peanuts back to the crowd so they could be tossed back again!

4. The English language did not originate in England. The language that became known as English was apparently first spoken by people living in what is now Germany. Tribes from this area brought their language with them when they invaded England. When we hear this early English, known as Anglo-Saxon or Old English, we find it hard to believe that it was the ancestor of Modern English. It sounds more like German.

5. The flu, or influenza, has been around for centuries. Its name reminds us that people once looked to the sky for its cause. The word *influenza* comes from the Italian word for *influence*, because people blamed their aches and fevers on the influence of the stars. In modern times, scientists have found a better explanation by looking through a microscope. The flu is caused by a tiny form of matter called a virus.

42

DRAWING CONCLUSIONS

NAME _____

1. You can tell that the writer thinks that—
   (A) there will always be some tramp steamers
   (B) the end of tramp steamers is no loss
   (C) tramp steamers should have a schedule
   (D) tramp steamers will one day be no more

2. The story gives—
   (A) ten reasons why hunters fear the rhino
   (B) at least three reasons why the rhino is dangerous
   (C) the reason for the rhino's mean temper
   (D) a complete list of the rhino's habits

3. From the story you cannot tell—
   (A) where the elephants were kept
   (B) how many fences were there
   (C) how many peanuts were lost
   (D) how the elephants returned the peanuts

4. The writer suggests that without Germany—
   (A) there would be no written language
   (B) the English language would be different today
   (C) there would be no English people
   (D) England would have no language

5. From the story you can tell that—
   (A) a virus can be seen with the naked eye
   (B) the stars once caused sickness
   (C) the author believes in scientific explanations
   (D) a cure for the flu has been discovered

43

IDENTIFYING INFERENCES

NAME _____

Read the short stories. On the opposite page, read the sentences after each story. Decide whether each sentence is true (T), false (F), or an inference (I). A true sentence tells a fact from the story. A false sentence tells something that is not true. An inference says something that is *probably* true, based on facts in the story. More than one sentence about each story may be true, false, or an inference. Place an X in the correct box to mark your answer.

1. Coleman trudged down the street, his hat thrown over his shoulder and his cap pulled down over his eyes. Dirt stains covered every inch of his uniform. He looked straight ahead, ignoring his friends who waved to him from the park. As he approached the house, his mother looked out the kitchen window. Just then Coleman lifted the bat over his shoulder and slammed it into the ground. Mrs. Nelson was surprised at her son's action.

2. Gwendolyn felt nervous as, from her position backstage, she watched her classmates perform. She had expected to be a little scared, but she had not thought she would feel such a mass of butterflies in her stomach. Mr. Kuru had given the whole class a lecture about opening-night jitters. He explained that people always feel nervous the first time they perform in front of an audience. "Wow! Was he right!" thought Gwendolyn. "I think I'll practice my lines one more time."

3. Sam knew how easy it was to let homework slide. He had a habit of waiting until just before bedtime to start his work. This meant that he was often too tired to concentrate on his assignments. "Maybe my teacher can help me organize my afterschool time the way he encouraged my friend, Donna, to work out a schedule," thought Sam. "If I do my homework immediately after school, maybe I'll do a better job." Sam decided to tell Mr. Needleman his idea. Sam was sure Mr. Needleman would have more good suggestions for getting the homework done.

4. Warren, now in his senior year, had studied very hard for the final math test. He had decided to work as hard as he could all month in order to get an A in math on his report card. Warren's father had helped him study. He had explained some formulas that Warren did not understand, and had also made up extra problems for Warren to work on. "The extra work really paid off," thought Warren. "I knew how to solve all the questions on the test. I'll bet I didn't make any mistakes at all."

5. "What's wrong with you?" asked Lloyd. "You look depressed."
   "I am depressed," replied Teddy forlornly. "Mother won't let me start a yard-cleaning service. My friend Alvin and I had a great idea for making money. We were going to put an advertisement in the paper telling people about our new service. Then they would hire us to take care of their yards."
   "Matt Johnson has that kind of business," said Lloyd, "but he's much older than you."

44

ANSWER KEY

NAME _____

IDENTIFYING INFERENCES

		T	F	I
1.	(A) Coleman's friends waved to him.			
	(B) Coleman was upset over the baseball game he had just played in.			
	(C) Mrs. Nelson was surprised to see Coleman throw down his hat.			
	(D) Coleman's uniform was spotless.			
2.	(A) Gwendolyn was worried that her nervousness would cause her to forget her part.			
	(B) Mr. Kanu knows that stage fright is to be expected.			
	(C) Gwendolyn was the first performer to go onstage.			
	(D) Gwendolyn disagreed with what Mr. Kanu had said about opening-night jitters.			
3.	(A) Mr. Needleman has a reputation for helping his students.			
	(B) Donna was Sam's friend.			
	(C) Sam was often too tired to give full attention to his studies.			
	(D) Donna had gotten no help from Mr. Needleman.			
4.	(A) Warren had done a lot of extra studying in math.			
	(B) Warren was in his senior year.			
	(C) Warren is going to get his A in math.			
	(D) Warren's father couldn't understand the formulas.			
5.	(A) Teddy's mother wanted Alvin and Teddy to start a yard-cleaning business.			
	(B) Teddy and Alvin wanted to put an ad in the paper.			
	(C) Matt Johnson has a yard-cleaning business.			
	(D) Lloyd thought that Teddy and Alvin were too young to start a yard-cleaning service.			

45

NAME _____

GETTING THE FACTS

Read the story, then, on the opposite page, circle the letter choice that best completes each sentence about the story.

Escape

"We're going to escape," said William Craft to his wife, Ellen. They had just witnessed another slave being flogged to death at the whipping post. From Macon, Georgia, they would have to flee a thousand miles north to reach freedom—but William had a plan!

They would escape by train while slave catchers searched for them in swamps. "You will dress as a young male planter," William chuckled. He drew a silk hat, a waistcoat, and trousers from a bag. Ellen's skin color was so fair that she had often been mistaken for white. "I will be your slave," William explained. "Just try to speak as little as possible," he cautioned.

On December 21, 1848, Ellen purchased tickets for herself and her "slave." Once on the train, Ellen was stunned. Beside her sat one of the most dreaded slave catchers—Willis Hughes. Hughes and another slave catcher, after getting off, recognized Ellen through the window. For the moment, however, the fugitives were safe. The train was speeding away.

They stayed at the finest hotel in Charleston, South Carolina. Everyone treated Ellen with great respect. She was the very image of a typical planter. The manager did not even ask her to register. William had put her arm in a sling because neither he nor Ellen had ever been taught to write.

The next morning the slave catchers arrived in Charleston, but William and Ellen were safely aboard the train. Only four more days to Baltimore, Maryland, the last stop before freedom! However, in Baltimore the ticket agent told Ellen she could not take her slave North without ownership papers.

Suddenly William had an inspiration. "I am taking young master to a doctor in Philadelphia," he explained. "Young master is sick."

At that moment another passenger said, "I know the young man. I have come with him all the way from Georgia." The agent let them go.

Ellen and William boarded the train to Philadelphia, Pennsylvania, and freedom. It was one of the most daring of all escapes from slavery.

46

NAME _____

GETTING THE FACTS

1. Ellen and William lived in the area of—
   - (A) Mobile, Alabama
   - (B) Miami, Florida
   - (C) Macon, Georgia
   - (D) Atlanta, Georgia
2. Freedom lay at a distance of—
   - (A) 1,000 miles
   - (B) 2,000 miles
   - (C) 900 miles
   - (D) 500 miles
3. Ellen was to dress as a young male—
   - (A) slave
   - (B) ticket agent
   - (C) manager
   - (D) planter
4. Ellen purchased train tickets on—
   - (A) January 5, 1959
   - (B) December 21, 1848
   - (C) May 20, 1789
   - (D) November 30, 1821
5. The man who sat beside Ellen was named—
   - (A) Moore
   - (B) Carroll
   - (C) Hughes
   - (D) Smith
6. They stayed at the finest hotel in—
   - (A) Philadelphia
   - (B) Macon
   - (C) Baltimore
   - (D) Charleston
7. Ellen's arm was in a—
   - (A) cast
   - (B) sling
   - (C) sleeve
   - (D) bandage
8. The slave catchers arrived in Charleston—
   - (A) the next morning
   - (B) the next afternoon
   - (C) that evening
   - (D) two days later
9. The ticket agent demanded—
   - (A) money
   - (B) papers
   - (C) tickets
   - (D) passengers
10. William announced he was taking Ellen to a—
    - (A) friend
    - (B) hospital
    - (C) doctor
    - (D) relative

47

NAME _____

GETTING THE MAIN IDEA

Read the stories, then, on the opposite page, circle the letter choice for the sentence that tells the main idea of the story.

1. Texas longhorns were not like the gentle, fat, slow-moving cattle of today. They were huge—weighing over a thousand pounds—and were almost as fast as deer. They had a fighting spirit, pointed horns that they enjoyed tossing, sharp hooves, and a deep dislike for anything in their way. The Texas longhorns were fierce animals that commanded respect from people—and even from grizzly bears!

2. Few people are aware of the huge size of Canada. It is the second largest country in the world. Only the Soviet Union is larger. Canada reaches one-fourth of the way around the world. It has more lakes than the rest of the world's countries combined. Yet there are but 24 million people in this vast land, only about as many as in the state of California.

3. The Haskell Opera House lies partly in the United States, partly in Canada. The entrance is in America, but the stage is in Canada. Local people tell about a man wanted by the American police. He was discovered performing on the stage of the Haskell Opera House. Since he stayed in the Canadian half of the building, and so was in a foreign country, American authorities couldn't arrest him!

4. Canada is more than a land of great beauty. It is also a land of vast forests. Lumber and the products that come from lumber make Canada a leader in world paper production. The pulp and paper industry continues to grow and is now Canada's leading industry.

5. Communication means a sharing of information. People communicate with each other in many ways. Much communication is face-to-face and silent. People smile and laugh. They shake hands. They wave. They squeeze a friend's hand to communicate sympathy or greetings. People share information about how they feel, often without as much as a single word.

48

NAME _____

GETTING THE MAIN IDEA

1. The paragraph tells mainly—
   - (A) how big the Texas longhorns were
   - (B) what Texas longhorns were like
   - (C) why grizzly bears ran away
   - (D) what the horns of the Texas longhorns were like
2. The paragraph tells mainly—
   - (A) where Canada is located
   - (B) why few people live in Canada
   - (C) how large Canada is
   - (D) how many lakes Canada has
3. The paragraph tells mainly—
   - (A) where the Haskell Opera House is located
   - (B) why the police wanted to arrest a performer
   - (C) what strange event occurred at the Haskell Opera House
   - (D) which part of the Haskell Opera House is in America
4. The paragraph tells mainly—
   - (A) how many trees there are
   - (B) why Canada has so many trees
   - (C) what Canada gets from its forests
   - (D) why Canada is so beautiful
5. The paragraph tells mainly—
   - (A) what information means
   - (B) how people communicate without words
   - (C) how people show sympathy by squeezing hands
   - (D) why words aren't important

49

NAME _____

FOLLOWING DIRECTIONS

Read each set of directions, then circle the letter choice that best answers the question about the directions.

DIRECTIONS: Relax and don't throw yourself into a panic. Concentrate on how you traveled. Mark a tree on all sides so that you can spot it from any direction. Then walk in a circle around the tree examining the surrounding area. Be sure to leave a note for your fellow hikers, telling them the direction in which you headed. Try to locate a stream. Follow it downstream; it will probably lead you to a town or village. Always look for high ground. Look and call out from a hill or tall tree. Follow telephone wires, power lines, and the sounds of cars; these will lead you to civilization. If possible, send up a smoke signal. Should darkness fall while you are still lost, stay where you are and look for shelter.

1. These directions show you how to—
   - (A) start a camping trip
   - (B) start a fire
   - (C) climb a tree
   - (D) react if you become lost
2. Before examining the surrounding ground,—
   - (A) find a stream
   - (B) mark a tree
   - (C) start a fire
   - (D) find shelter
3. Should you find a stream, follow it—
   - (A) upstream
   - (B) toward telephone lines
   - (C) downstream
   - (D) even after dark
4. If darkness falls and you're still lost,—
   - (A) follow the sound of autos
   - (B) locate a stream
   - (C) mark a tree
   - (D) stay where you are

50

ANSWER KEY

NAME _____

USING THE CONTEXT

Read each set of sentences. In each set of sentences, there are two blanks. Circle the letter choice for the correct word that goes in each blank.

The record cold for the United States was eighty degrees below zero in Prospect Creek, Alaska, in July of 1983. But this (1) _____ was balmy compared to that (2) _____ at Vostok, a Russian Antarctic station. Here the temperatures are the lowest on Earth—with a record low of 128.6 degrees below zero!

1. (A) thermometer (B) humidity (C) temperature (D) event
2. (A) approved (B) prescribed (C) caught (D) registered

Hurricanes create floods. When these storms move in toward shore, they whip up huge waves. These waves can be highly dangerous. More (3) _____ are caused by (4) _____ than by wind.

3. (A) deaths (B) accidents (C) rescues (D) bruises
4. (A) confusion (B) lifesaving (C) drowning (D) fear

The common house cat played an important role in winning the West. Rats were (5) _____ grain supplies maintained for the army. In desperation, cats were ordered from the East. The new arrivals kept the rat population under (6) _____.

5. (A) routing (B) harvesting (C) entering (D) destroying
6. (A) guard (B) scrutiny (C) supervision (D) control

Transportation is one of the basic needs of people. Its importance can hardly be measured. From earliest times inventive (7) _____ have been seeking to improve the (8) _____ of moving persons and goods from place to place.

7. (A) tools (B) minds (C) clubs (D) trucks
8. (A) methods (B) differences (C) belongings (D) tricks

Gray or white hair is not caused by worrying or even by aging. People (9) _____ certain genes that determine when and how much gray hair they will get. It can start as early as the teens or whenever the hair glands decrease their (10) _____ of coloring matter.

9. (A) annex (B) inherit (C) revise (D) vote
10. (A) devotion (B) campaign (C) production (D) appointment

51

NAME _____

GETTING THE MAIN IDEA

Read the stories, then, on the opposite page, circle the letter choice for the sentence that tells the main idea of the story.

1. The human body can adapt itself remarkably to difficult conditions of living. For example, people who live high in the Andes Mountains, where the air is very thin, have an extra quart of blood in their bodies to help them get enough oxygen. Also, from years of walking barefoot in the cold, these people have grown extra blood vessels in their feet. They can walk barefoot even in snow without discomfort.

2. We think of the collie, German shepherd, Great Dane, Newfoundland, and Saint Bernard as fun-loving pets. Once these famous breeds were just work dogs with special duties to perform. The collie and German shepherd were flock tenders. The Great Dane was a property guard. The Newfoundland was the world's champion lifesaver. The Saint Bernard broke trails for people over deep snowfalls in the Alps mountains.

3. Perhaps the world's most violent snowstorm is the purga. This dreaded blizzard sweeps over northern Siberia in winter. Its violence is so great that people cannot open their eyes. Many people even report difficulty in standing upright. People caught in this blinding storm often become lost and freeze to death within yards of the doorways to their homes.

4. Ancient papyrus sheets have been discovered in the sands of Egypt. They have been preserved by the dryness of the climate. One sheet contains a laundry list: "fine tunics 2, dalmatics 2, breeches 2, felt slippers 1, carpetbag, ground-sheet, small pillow, etc." A letter sent home by a school child ends with a postscript, "Please feed my pigeons." How like our own lives are the daily lives of these people!

5. There is a worm in the sea that is actually a living fishline! This is the fishline worm. It can be found curled up under a rock. It looks small, but when it uncoils it is eighty feet long. The sharp teeth of the worm attach themselves to a small fish. Once they do, they never let go. Finally the fish tires of fighting the long worm. The fishline worm then devours its catch.

52

NAME _____

GETTING THE MAIN IDEA

1. The paragraph tells mainly—
(A) how Andean people get cold from walking barefoot
(B) what the air is like in the Andes
(C) how people's bodies can adjust to a climate
(D) how much oxygen everyone's blood needs

2. The paragraph tells mainly—
(A) which dogs are fun-loving pets
(B) where some dogs were used to guard property
(C) why some dogs were used to do work
(D) how certain pet dogs were once work animals

3. The paragraph tells mainly—
(A) how often the purga occurs
(B) what happens in winter
(C) why people can't open their eyes
(D) why the purga is dreaded

4. The paragraph tells mainly—
(A) where papyrus sheets were discovered
(B) how the papyrus sheets were preserved
(C) how one school child of ancient Egypt wrote
(D) what the papyrus sheets reveal

5. The paragraph tells mainly—
(A) how the worm uncoils
(B) what kinds of fish are caught
(C) how fishline worms are caught
(D) how a worm catches fish

53

NAME _____

DRAWING CONCLUSIONS

Read the short stories, then, on the opposite page, circle the letter choice that describes something you can tell from the information in the story. Use clues in each story to draw a conclusion to find the correct answer.

1. Long ago, passenger pigeons flew over North America in such vast numbers that they actually darkened the sun as they passed. In a single flock there were often more than a billion passenger pigeons! Single nesting areas were often thirty or more miles long and three to six miles wide. Today, the passenger pigeon is extinct. The last survivor of the breed died in a Cincinnati zoo in 1914.

2. In 1959, a British engineer invented a transportation machine called the hovercraft. It is a boat-shaped, flat-bottomed carrier that rides on a cushion of air created by motors. One special feature of the hovercraft is its ability to ride over both land and water at heights low enough for easy viewing. This has been useful in the exploration of swampy rivers such as the Amazon.

3. The most beautiful of all horses is the Arabian Asil. Its neck is gracefully arched. Its head is small and delicate with eyes that are large, fiery, and far apart. Its small ears point inward. This horse has a full, flowing tail that it carries high, and its skin is a shiny black. The Arabian Asil is one of the most beautiful of all creatures.

4. The area that birds defend against other birds of their own species is called a territory. By controlling such an area, the bird protects its family from other birds of the same species. It also insures both food and nesting materials in this way. The size of the territory depends on many factors, such as the amount of food available, the type of bird, and even its size.

5. Down through the ages flea circuses have been used to attract people to fairs and markets. Fleas are dressed in tiny costumes. Some are tightrope walkers. Others take part in chariot races and tugs of war. Today, most of these circuses have disappeared. However, the name remains in the so-called flea market, an open-air market in which various goods are sold.

54

NAME _____

DRAWING CONCLUSIONS

1. From the story you cannot tell—
(A) how large the flocks were
(B) when the passenger pigeon became extinct
(C) why the passenger pigeon died out
(D) where the last passenger pigeon died

2. From the story you can tell that the hovercraft—
(A) could be used for exploring a chain of islands
(B) resembles a helicopter
(C) is unsafe in stormy weather
(D) creates less noise and pollution than an automobile

3. A good name for the Arabian Asil would be—
(A) Star of the North
(B) Brown Eyes
(C) Speedy
(D) Black Beauty

4. The story gives—
(A) ten reasons for bird territories
(B) the writer's opinion of birds
(C) three reasons for bird territories
(D) the size of most bird territories

5. Fleas were helpful in—
(A) scattering crowds
(B) drawing crowds
(C) annoying crowds
(D) calming crowds

55

NAME _____

IDENTIFYING INFERENCES

Read the story stories. On the opposite page, read the sentences about each story. Decide whether each sentence is true (T), false (F), or an inference (I). A true sentence tells a fact from the story. A false sentence tells something that is not true. An inference says something that is probably true, based on facts in the story. More than one sentence about each story may be true, false, or an inference. Place an X in the correct box to mark your answer.

1. Candice had paused at the front door for a few seconds, as if hoping to gain entrance. Her shiny black hair glistened in the sun. Her light green eyes gazed around expectantly. Then she turned and began walking very slowly away from the house. She stopped a moment to stretch her legs and back.
"Are you hungry?" asked the boy in the house, opening the door. "Come on, I'll give you something to eat." Without saying a word in reply, Candice bounded into the house and headed straight for the kitchen. A fish dinner and some warm milk awaited her.

2. Jeannie broke the surface of the water with a gasp. She spotted the judges on the shore and began stroking steadily toward them. As she raised her head to inhale, she caught glimpses of Nell and Cheryl. Nell was several yards behind her, but Cheryl was even with her. "Should I make the push now," thought Jeannie, "or wait until the last ten yards?" Jeannie remembered that Cheryl often lost strength during the last quarter of a race—which was right about now. "Here I go!" exclaimed Jeannie.

3. "What will you get Mom for her birthday?" Eddie asked Monica.
"I've been thinking about getting her some new gardening tools," said Monica. "The ones she has are all bent and rusty."
"Well, if we went in together on a present," suggested Eddie, "we could get her what she really wants and needs."
"What's that?" asked Monica.
"A gas lawn mower," replied Eddie. "You know how she knocks herself out pushing that old hand mower around the yard."
"Great idea!" agreed Monica.

4. "I wonder why they're building that skyscraper backwards?" said Mr. Heath. "It doesn't seem logical to complete it from the top down."
"I read a brief news article about that new building method," said Mrs. Drew. "First they build the frame. Then they hang the outer skin of the building on the frame from the top down. The outside of the building comes in sections. Each section has hooks that let it hang on the frame."
"That's very interesting," said Mr. Heath. "Do they always begin hanging the sections from the top, or could they start anywhere?"
"I've no idea," said Mrs. Drew. "I've told all I know about it."

5. Jennifer's father hammered in the last stake and looked doubtfully at the tent. "I see we have another small tear in the side. I'd better fix it right now. No telling if we might have a little rain tonight."
"Will the tent be all right, Dad?" asked Jennifer.
"Oh, sure, but we'll retire 'old faithful' here after this camping trip and get a new one for next summer."

56

73

ANSWER KEY

Worksheet 1 (page 57)

IDENTIFYING INFERENCES

1. (A) Candice is a cat. — F
   (B) The boy gave Candice a fish dinner and some warm milk. — T
   (C) Candice turned and walked away from the house after the boy called her. — F
   (D) Candice had eaten at the boy's house before. — I

2. (A) Jeannie had a good chance of winning her race. — T
   (B) Jeannie was several yards ahead of Nell. — F
   (C) Cheryl always sped up during the last quarter. — F
   (D) Jeannie didn't think Nell would win the race. — I

3. (A) Monica had been thinking about getting her mother some gardening tools. — I
   (B) Eddie wanted to get the old hand mower sharpened. — F
   (C) Mother's present gardening tools are rusty. — T
   (D) Mother prefers useful presents to impractical gifts. — I

4. (A) Mrs. Drew told Mr. Heath what she knew about the building method. — F
   (B) The news article hadn't given full details of the new method. — I
   (C) Mr. Heath wondered why the builders were constructing the skyscraper backwards. — T
   (D) Mr. Heath wasn't interested in the building method. — F

5. (A) Jennifer wondered if the tent would be all right. — T
   (B) The tent had a small tear in the side. — F
   (C) The family had been camping often before. — I
   (D) Jennifer's father referred to the tent as "old ironsides." — T

57

Worksheet 2 (page 58)

DETECTING THE SEQUENCE

Read the story. As you read it, look for clues that let you know the order in which things happened. Then, on the opposite page, circle the letter choice that best answers the question about the sequence of events.

Mount St. Helens' Eruption

At 8:32 A.M. on May 18, 1980, an earthquake ripped through Mount St. Helens. The north side of the mountain slid away in the quake, and tons of earth crashed down the slope toward the North Toutle River. Meanwhile, gases exploded out of the mountain. Two hundred miles away, people heard the roar. A powerful wave of gas and steam rolled through the sky at the speed of a plane, leveling two hundred square miles of trees. Next came a fiery blanket of ash and a hail of ice and rocks. The ash turned the sky gray and spread over a huge area. All this happened within minutes.

This force of the eruption of Mount St. Helens took even scientists by surprise. They had been watching the Washington mountain since March 21, 1980, when earthquakes had begun shaking it. Scientists had long known that this volcano might erupt. As far back as 1831, it had begun to spew forth different combinations of steam, ash, mud, and lava. These eruptions had continued for twenty-five years. Mount St. Helens then sat quietly for over 120 years. However, a number of geologists predicted an eruption in the twentieth century.

Reporters and geologists hurried to Mount St. Helens after the earthquakes began in March 1980. However, the mountain stayed fairly quiet through April. A second crater appeared near one already there. Then the two blended into one large bowl, which measured 1,700 feet across and 850 feet deep. By May 10, the volcano's activity had increased, and a large bulge formed on its north face. The bulge grew by five feet a day. Scientists expected an eruption soon, but they had no idea it would come with such magnitude and speed.

The eruption on May 18 damaged a vast area. The earth that slid down Mount St. Helens' north slope finally came to rest in the North Toutle Valley, covering the valley with mud and water. The cloud of ash lasted longer and spread much farther. It left inches of choking ash on towns near Mount St. Helens. Soon wind transported the ash cloud east, and within three days it had crossed North America.

Another major eruption of Mount St. Helens is unlikely for thousands of years. Other mountains nearby have showed signs of activity, though. In July 1980, more than fifty small quakes shook Mount Hood. Scientists continue to keep close watch. As they learned from Mount St. Helens, nature's force should not be taken lightly.

58

Worksheet 3 (page 59)

DETECTING THE SEQUENCE

1. Which of these events happened first?
   (A) Mount St. Helens began spewing forth combinations of steam, ash, mud, and lava.
   (B) An earthquake ripped through Mount St. Helens.
   (C) Reporters and geologists hurried to Mount St. Helens.
   (D) The north side of the mountain slid away, sending tons of earth crashing downward.

2. Which of these events happened last?
   (A) Earth from the volcano came to rest in the North Toutle Valley.
   (B) Wind transported the ash cloud east.
   (C) More than fifty small quakes shook Mount Hood. ✓
   (D) A bulge formed on the north face of Mount St. Helens.

3. What happened at the same time tons of earth crashed down the slope of Mount St. Helens?
   (A) A hail of ice and rocks fell.
   (B) Gases exploded out of the mountain. ✓
   (C) A second crater appeared on the slope.
   (D) A bulge formed on the north face.

4. What happened after a blanket of ash came from the mountain?
   (A) The sky turned gray. ✓
   (B) An earthquake shook the mountain.
   (C) Gas and steam rolled through the sky.
   (D) Reporters and geologists hurried to the mountain.

5. When did a large bulge form on the face of Mount St. Helens?
   (A) after the north face slid away
   (B) before a second crater appeared
   (C) while an eruption took place
   (D) after earthquakes began shaking the mountain ✓

59

Worksheet 4 (page 60)

IDENTIFYING INFERENCES

Read the short stories. On the opposite page, read the sentences about each story. Decide whether each sentence is true (T), false (F), or an inference (I). A true sentence tells a fact from the story. A false sentence tells something that is not true. An inference says something that is probably true, based on facts in the story. More than one sentence about each story may be true, false, or an inference. Place an X in the correct box to mark your answer.

1. "What do you think about the announcement the President made last night?" Joe asked his friend, Hank.
   "What announcement?" Hank asked. "I haven't heard anything about it."
   Joe was surprised. "Are you serious? It was the main news in the papers and on the radio this morning."
   "Oh, really? It must be quite important. I'll bet you had a chance to hear the final score of the hockey game on the news, too. How did it turn out?"

2. "I'm going to sign up for the CPR class today," Nancy told Rachel.
   "What's CPR?" Rachel wanted to know.
   "Cardiopulmonary resuscitation," said Nancy. "It's emergency treatment for someone who can't breathe. A person having a heart attack needs it. Don't you remember when Jean's father had a heart attack, and she saved his life because she knew how to do CPR? Well, I've been wanting to learn ever since then."

3. "As you all know," stated Coach Hanks of the Bears, "this is our last game of the season. We've waited a long time to play the Cougars again, so let's go onto that field and give it all we've got!"
   "Don't worry, Coach Hanks," yelled Tom. "This time the Bears will be on the winning side, and the Cougars will be on the losing side. No more second-place finishes for us!"

4. Tony and his parents had sat patiently through all the greetings and announcements on the program. Tony had hardly paid attention while the names of the second- and third-place winners were announced. Tony suddenly sat up straight, though, when he heard the president of the service club say, "And now, ladies and gentlemen, it is my honor to present the grand prize." The president paused a moment and cleared her throat. As she made the announcement, a smile broke out on Tony's face.

5. Dana shifted in the saddle and looked at the time. They'd been riding for two hours. "Are we almost there?" Dana called to Fran.
   "It won't be long now," said Fran encouragingly. "The ranch is just over that rise, to the left of that clump of cactuses. And there's a water tank ahead, where we can rest in the shade and have some cool water."

60

Worksheet 5 (page 61)

IDENTIFYING INFERENCES

1. (A) Hank is interested more in sports news than in political news. — I
   (B) Joe asked Hank his opinion of the President's announcement. — T
   (C) Hank said he hadn't heard about the President's announcement. — T
   (D) Hank was interested in learning how the tennis match had turned out. — F

2. (A) Jean had saved her father's life with CPR. — F
   (B) Rachel wanted to know what CPR is. — T
   (C) Nancy said that CPR is emergency treatment for someone who can't breathe. — T
   (D) Nancy likes to be prepared for emergencies. — I

3. (A) Tom is on the Bears' team. — T
   (B) This is the Bears' first game of the season. — F
   (C) Tom's team is playing in a championship game. — I
   (D) Tom told the coach not to worry. — T

4. (A) Tony was the winner of the grand prize. — I
   (B) The president cleared her throat before announcing the winner of the grand prize. — T
   (C) Tony's parents were at the program. — T
   (D) The second- and third-place winners were announced last. — F

5. (A) Fran said there was a water tank ahead. — T
   (B) The ranch is in the desert. — I
   (C) Dana was getting tired of riding. — I
   (D) Dana and Fran had been riding for ten hours. — F

61

Worksheet 6 (page 62)

PROGRESS CHECK

Exercising Your Skill

A **conclusion** is a decision or judgment you make that is based on facts and information. **Syllogisms** organize information so that readers can draw a conclusion based on facts. In a syllogism, all the information you need to draw a conclusion is given in two statements called **premises**. Read the two syllogisms below. Note the underlined words and the letters above them. Think about the premises in each syllogism. The first syllogism is correct; the second is incorrect.

	Syllogism 1	Syllogism 2
	A B	A B
First premise:	All horses eat hay.	All horses eat hay.
	C A	C B
Second premise:	Jingle is a horse.	A deer eats hay.
	C B	C A
Conclusion:	Jingle eats hay.	A deer is a horse.

The pattern AB, CA, CB and thinking about the premises will help you recognize a correct syllogism.

Now read each of the following syllogisms. Write *correct* if the syllogism is correct and *incorrect* if it is incorrect.

1. First premise: All tarantulas are spiders.
   Second premise: All spiders have eight legs.
   Conclusion: Tarantulas have eight legs.
   correct

2. First premise: All languages have meaning.
   Second premise: The Russian language has meaning.
   Conclusion: All languages are Russian.
   incorrect

3. First premise: All snakes shed their skin.
   Second premise: A boa constrictor is a snake.
   Conclusion: A boa constrictor sheds its skin.
   correct

62

74

ANSWER KEY

NAME _____

PROGRESS CHECK

Exploring Language

Read each of the following syllogisms. For each pair of premises, write a conclusion.

1. First premise: All cats have whiskers.
   Second premise: A lion is a kind of cat.
   Conclusion: A lion has whiskers.

2. First premise: All citrus fruits contain vitamin C.
   Second premise: An orange is a citrus fruit.
   Conclusion: An orange contains vitamin C.

3. First premise: Only a native-born American can become president of the United States.
   Second premise: Ronald Reagan was president of the United States from 1981 to 1989.
   Conclusion: Ronald Reagan is a native-born American.

4. First premise: All reference books give factual information.
   Second premise: An encyclopedia is a reference book.
   Conclusion: An encyclopedia gives factual information.

5. First premise: Only living things can breathe.
   Second premise: A rock is not a living thing.
   Conclusion: A rock cannot breathe.

63

NAME _____

USING THE CONTEXT

Read each set of sentences. In each set of sentences, there are two blanks. Circle the letter choice for the correct word that goes in each blank.

Bees, wasps, and yellow jackets notice what people wear. They are especially attracted to clothes with bright colors and floral (1) _____. They are also (2) _____ toward people who wear perfume or hair spray. People who don't want to be stung will wear neutral-colored clothing and forget perfume and hair spray.

1. (A) notepaper　(B) wallpaper　(C) names　(D) patterns
2. (A) proposed　(B) labeled　(C) lured　(D) blushed

In China purple is the color of (3) _____. An American manufacturer once packaged chewing gum in a purple wrapper. When he attempted to market it in China, he discovered sales were poor. The Chinese believed the gum could only be chewed at (4) _____.

3. (A) life　(B) spring　(C) disease　(D) death
4. (A) games　(B) funerals　(C) dances　(D) parades

If you were told that suits weigh less today than they did thirty years ago, would you believe it? It is a fact. Men's suits, for example, weighed five pounds in 1930. Men's suits today weigh less than two pounds. (5) _____ woolens are being replaced by (6) _____ materials.

5. (A) Smart　(B) Coarse　(C) Clever　(D) Heavy
6. (A) massive　(B) drab　(C) lighter　(D) weighty

Criminals prefer to work at night. Darkness gives them the protective covering they need, and their chances of being (7) _____ or caught are considerably lessened. Since other people are usually asleep or less alert, criminals can work at night without unnecessary (8) _____.

7. (A) added　(B) identified　(C) awakened　(D) tired
8. (A) interference　(B) talking　(C) directions　(D) noise

Early pioneer homes often stood many miles apart, with nothing between but forests. A visitor was a rare treat, and pioneer families were happy to (9) _____ their (10) _____ to any stranger who happened along. A guest bearing news or a good tale was particularly welcome.

9. (A) offer　(B) divide　(C) question　(D) consider
10. (A) animals　(B) hospitality　(C) stories　(D) work

64

McGraw-Hill Consumer Products

The skills taught in school are now available at home!
These award-winning software titles meet school guidelines and are based on
The McGraw-Hill Companies classroom software titles.

MATH GRADES 1 & 2

These math programs are a great way to teach and reinforce skills used in everyday situations. Fun, friendly characters need help with their math skills. Everyone's friend, Nubby the stubby pencil, will help kids master the math in the Numbers Quiz show. Foggy McHammer, a carpenter, needs some help building his playhouse so that all the boards will fit together! Julio Bambino's kitchen antics will surely burn his pastries if you don't help him set the clock timer correctly! We can't forget Turbo Tomato, a fruit with a passion for adventure, who needs help calculating his daredevil stunts.

Math Grades 1 & 2 use a tested, proven approach to reinforcing your child's math skills while keeping him or her intrigued with Nubby and his collection of crazy friends.

TITLE	ISBN
Grade 1: Nubby's Quiz Show	1-57768-321-8
Grade 2: Foggy McHammer's Treehouse	1-57768-322-6

Available in jewel case only (no box included)

MISSION MASTERS™ MATH AND LANGUAGE ARTS

The Mission Masters™—Pauline, Rakeem, Mia, and T.J.—need your help. The Mission Masters™ are a team of young agents working for the Intelliforce Agency, a high-level cooperative whose goal is to maintain order on our rather unruly planet. From within the agency's top secret Command Control Center, the agency's central computer, M5, has detected a threat...and guess what—you're the agent assigned to the mission!

MISSION MASTERS™ MATH
GRADES 3, 4, & 5

This series of exciting activities encourages young mathematicians to challenge themselves and their math skills to overcome the perils of villains and other planetary threats. Skills reinforced include: analyzing and solving real-world problems, estimation, measurements, geometry, whole numbers, fractions, graphs, and patterns.

TITLE	ISBN
Grade 3: Mission Masters™ Defeat Dirty D!	1-57768-323-5
Grade 4: Mission Masters™ Alien Encounter	1-57768-324-2
Grade 5: Mission Masters™ Meet Mudflat Moe	1-57768-325-0

Available in jewel case only (no box included)

MISSION MASTERS™ LANGUAGE ARTS
GRADES 3, 4, & 5

This series invites children to apply their language skills to defeat unscrupulous characters and to overcome other earthly dangers. Skills reinforced include: language mechanics and usage, punctuation, spelling, vocabulary, reading comprehension, and creative writing.

TITLE	ISBN
Grade 3: Mission Masters™ Freezing Frenzy	1-57768-343-9
Grade 4: Mission Masters™ Network Nightmare	1-57768-344-7
Grade 5: Mission Masters™ Mummy Mysteries	1-57768-345-5

Available in jewel case only (no box included)

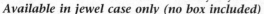

BASIC SKILLS BUILDER K to 2 – THE MAGIC APPLEHOUSE

At the Magic Applehouse, children discover that Abigail Appleseed runs a deliciously successful business selling apple pies, tarts, and other apple treats. Enthusiasm grows as children join in the fun of helping Abigail run her business. Along the way they'll develop computer and entrepreneurial skills to last a lifetime. They will run their own business – all while they're having bushels of fun!

TITLE	ISBN
Basic Skills Builder –The Magic Applehouse	1-57768-312-9

Available in jewel case only (no box included)

TEST PREP – SCORING HIGH

This grade-based testing software will help prepare your child for standardized achievement tests given by his or her school. Scoring High specifically targets the skills required for success on the Stanford Achievement Test (SAT) for grades three through eight. Lessons and test questions follow the same format and cover the same content areas as questions appearing on the actual SAT tests. The practice tests are modeled after the SAT test-taking experience with similar directions, number of questions per section, and bubble-sheet answer choices.

Scoring High is a child's first-class ticket to a winning score on standardized achievement tests!

TITLE	ISBN
Grades 3 to 5: Scoring High Test Prep	1-57768-316-1
Grades 6 to 8: Scoring High Test Prep	1-57768-317-X

Available in jewel case only (no box included)

SCIENCE

Mastering the principles of both physical and life science has never been so FUN for kids grades six and above as it is while they are exploring McGraw-Hill's edutainment software!

TITLE	ISBN
Grades 6 & up: Life Science	1-57768-336-6
Grades 8 & up: Physical Science	1-57768-308-0

Available in jewel case only (no box included)

REFERENCE

The National Museum of Women in the Arts has teamed with McGraw-Hill Consumer Products to bring you this superb collection available for your enjoyment on CD-ROM.

This special collection is a visual diary of 200 women artists from the Renaissance to the present, spanning 500 years of creativity.

You will discover the art of women who excelled in all the great art movements of history. Artists who pushed the boundaries of abstract, genre, landscape, narrative, portrait, and still-life styles; as well as artists forced to push the societal limits placed on women through the ages.

Most titles for Windows 3.1™, Windows '95™ & '98™, and Macintosh™.

TITLE	ISBN
Women in the Arts	1-57768-010-3

Available in boxed version only

Visit us on the Internet at:

www.MHkids.com

Or call 800-298-4119 for your local retailer.

McGraw-Hill
Consumer Products

All our workbooks meet school curriculum guidelines and correspond to
The McGraw-Hill Companies classroom textbooks.

SPECTRUM SERIES

DOLCH Sight Word Activities

The DOLCH Sight Word Activities Workbooks use the classic Dolch list of 220 basic vocabulary words that make up from 50% to 75% of all reading matter that children ordinarily encounter. Since these words are ordinarily recognized on sight, they are called *sight words*. Volume 1 includes 110 sight words. Volume 2 covers the remainder of the list. Over 160 pages.

TITLE	ISBN
Grades K-1 Vol. 1	1-57768-429-X
Grades K-1 Vol. 2	1-57768-439-7

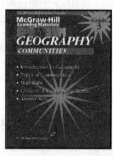

GEOGRAPHY

Full-color, three-part lessons strengthen geography knowledge and map reading skills. Focusing on five geographic themes including location, place, human/environmental interaction, movement, and regions. Over 150 pages. Glossary of geographical terms and answer key included.

TITLE	ISBN
Gr 3, Communities	1-57768-153-3
Gr 4, Regions	1-57768-154-1
Gr 5, USA	1-57768-155-X
Gr 6, World	1-57768-156-8

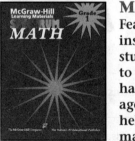

MATH

Features easy-to-follow instructions that give students a clear path to success. This series has comprehensive coverage of the basic skills, helping children to master math fundamentals. Over 150 pages. Answer key included.

TITLE	ISBN
Grade 1	1-57768-111-8
Grade 2	1-57768-112-6
Grade 3	1-57768-113-4
Grade 4	1-57768-114-2
Grade 5	1-57768-115-0
Grade 6	1-57768-116-9
Grade 7	1-57768-117-7
Grade 8	1-57768-118-5

PHONICS

Provides everything children need to build multiple skills in language. Focusing on phonics, structural analysis, and dictionary skills, this series also offers creative ideas for using phonics and word study skills in other language arts. Over 200 pages. Answer key included.

TITLE	ISBN
Grade K	1-57768-120-7
Grade 1	1-57768-121-5
Grade 2	1-57768-122-3
Grade 3	1-57768-123-1
Grade 4	1-57768-124-X
Grade 5	1-57768-125-8
Grade 6	1-57768-126-6

READING

This full-color series creates an enjoyable reading environment, even for below-average readers. Each book contains captivating content, colorful characters, and compelling illustrations, so children are eager to find out what happens next. Over 150 pages. Answer key included.

TITLE	ISBN
Grade K	1-57768-130-4
Grade 1	1-57768-131-2
Grade 2	1-57768-132-0
Grade 3	1-57768-133-9
Grade 4	1-57768-134-7
Grade 5	1-57768-135-5
Grade 6	1-57768-136-3

SPELLING

This full-color series links spelling to reading and writing and increases skills in words and meanings, consonant and vowel spellings, and proofreading practice. Over 200 pages. Speller dictionary and answer key included.

TITLE	ISBN
Grade 1	1-57768-161-4
Grade 2	1-57768-162-2
Grade 3	1-57768-163-0
Grade 4	1-57768-164-9
Grade 5	1-57768-165-7
Grade 6	1-57768-166-5

WRITING

Lessons focus on creative and expository writing using clearly stated objectives and pre-writing exercises. Eight essential reading skills are applied. Activities include main idea, sequence, comparison, detail, fact and opinion, cause and effect, and making a point. Over 130 pages. Answer key included.

TITLE	ISBN
Grade 1	1-57768-141-X
Grade 2	1-57768-142-8
Grade 3	1-57768-143-6
Grade 4	1-57768-144-4
Grade 5	1-57768-145-2
Grade 6	1-57768-146-0
Grade 7	1-57768-147-9
Grade 8	1-57768-148-7

TEST PREP
From the Nation's #1 Testing Company

Prepares children to do their best on current editions of the five major standardized tests. Activities reinforce test-taking skills through examples, tips, practice, and timed exercises. Subjects include reading, math, and language. Over 150 pages. Answer key included.

TITLE	ISBN
Grade 1	1-57768-101-0
Grade 2	1-57768-102-9
Grade 3	1-57768-103-7
Grade 4	1-57768-104-5
Grade 5	1-57768-105-3
Grade 6	1-57768-106-1
Grade 7	1-57768-107-X
Grade 8	1-57768-108-8

LANGUAGE ARTS

Encourages creativity and builds confidence by making writing fun! Seventy-two four-part lessons strengthen writing skills by focusing on parts of speech, word usage, sentence structure, punctuation, and proofreading. Each level includes a *Writer's Handbook* at the end of the book that offers writing tips. This series is based on the highly respected SRA/McGraw-Hill language arts series. More than 180 full-color pages. *Available March 2000.*

TITLE	ISBN
Grade 2	1-57768-472-9
Grade 3	1-57768-473-7
Grade 4	1-57768-474-5
Grade 5	1-57768-475-3
Grade 6	1-57768-476-1